CS 159

Programming Applications for Engineers

Spring 2018

William Crum
Department of Computer Science
Purdue University

ISBN 978-1-60904-702-3

Published by

Stipes Publishing L.L.C,
204 West University Avenue
Champaign, Illinois 61820

CS 159: Programming Applications for Engineers — Spring 2018
ISBN: 978-1-60904-702-3

Table of Contents

Course Information 1

Course Programming & Documentation Standards 11

Fall 2017 Old Exams and Solutions. 23

Lecture Notes. 69

UNIX Handout 239

VI Editor 240

Lecture Quiz Difficulty Report 241

CS 159—Important Information... 243

CS 159 - Programming Applications for Engineers, Spring 2018

Course Objectives:

CS 159 introduces the tools of software development that have become essential for innovative and creative problem solving in engineering. Educators and employers agree that it is important for future engineering professionals to be able to function as part of a technical team and develop the ability to communicate advanced technical concepts. CS 159 will require students to work in assigned teams for all lab assignments. Educational research informs us that structured collaboration leads to increased learning gains for all students participating in an introductory programming course.

- **Collaboration is a requirement of the course.** You will be assigned to your teams by your lab instructor.

CS 159 explores the concepts of programming using a language and environment that are new to most students. Our objectives are for you to recognize how programming concepts are common to the various languages to which you are exposed to in the first-year engineering program and how those concepts can be used to solve a problem.

Course Prerequisites and Preparation:

The University expects students to place 2-3 hours outside of class per week in preparation for each credit hour of a course. The key to success in this course requires participation in lecture and lab, preparation and regular review of course materials, and the setting of goals to start and complete all assignments well in advance of the due date. **The most successful students in previous offerings of CS 159 report habits such as attending every lecture, reading the text, and daily code writing that goes beyond the minimum of completing assignments.**

- **CS 159 does have a co-requisite of ENGR 131.** Authorized equivalent courses or consent of instructor may be used in satisfying the course co-requisite.
- **What does the co-requisite imply?** ENGR 131 as a co-requisite would imply that you are or have been (1) enrolled in a course that will expose you to the fundamentals of MATLAB or (2) have had some previous programming experience in a language such as C, C++, or JAVA. Most students in CS 159 will also be enrolled ENGR 132 where they are introduced to writing programs in MATLAB using structured programming concepts.

Supplemental Instruction:

There are Supplemental Instruction (SI) student sessions available for this course. These student groups are open to anyone enrolled in this course who would like to stay current with the course material and understand it better. Attendance at these sessions is voluntary, but for the maximum benefit you should attend regularly. Time and locations for the study sessions can be found on-line: http://www.purdue.edu/si.

Students who attend these interactive sessions will find themselves working with peers as they compare notes, demonstrate and discuss relevant problems and important concepts, and share study and test-taking strategies.

- Students are asked to arrive with their student ID card, lecture notes, and be prepared to participate with others during these sessions.
- SI leaders are undergraduate students who have previously been very successful in the course and model their strategies for success to current students.
- Every session will cover new material! No two sessions will repeat the same content.

Course Staff:

Instructor: William Crum Office Location: HAAS G-26	Instructor Office Hours (HAAS G-26): • Monday 9:00am – 10:30am • Wednesday 10:30am – 12:00pm	Additional TA Office Hours (HAAS G-25):
TA Evening Hours: Sunday through Thursday 7:00pm – 9:00pm Location: SC 189		

Please visit during office hours for any administrative concerns regarding the course.

- If you have a concern then it is expected that you make the effort to visit office hours.

Important Dates:

Midterm Exam #1	Midterm Exam #2	Final Exam	Academic Calendar
Date: Tuesday February 20 **Time:** 6:30 – 7:30pm **Location:** Hall of Music	**Date:** Tuesday March 27 **Time:** 8:00 – 9:30pm **Location:** Hall of Music	**Date:** **Time:** **Location:**	**Last Day to Drop:** Friday March 9, 2018

- The final exam may be on Saturday May 5th from 3:30 – 5:30pm. Requests for alternative exam offerings will not be considered for reasons other than those outlined by the regulations of the university. **Please make your travel arrangements accordingly.**

Blackboard (mycourses.purdue.edu)**:**

All relevant class information, updates, and announcements will be available on the Blackboard site.

In the event of a major campus emergency, course requirements, deadlines, and grading percentages are subject to changes that may be necessitated by a revised semester calendar or other circumstances.

- In case of a campus emergency, check Blackboard, do not email or call course staff. Follow all official university issued instructions. See https://www.purdue.edu/ehps/emergency_preparedness/ for more information.
- The instructor reserves the right to revise the syllabus and will provide notice.

Course Required Materials:

- Computer Science, A Structured Programming Approach Using C, Forouzan and Gilberg, THIRD EDITION, ISBN: 0-534-49132-4
- Programming Applications for Engineers Course Packet (Spring 2018 edition)
- iClicker response pad

Assignments:

Lab Assignments (12 total, 5 points each):

Lab assignments are to be completed **collaboratively** in your assigned lab groups and each of these lab programming assignments will be due 30 minutes prior to your next lab meeting. You will serve on a total of three different lab teams during the semester with each collaborating on four consecutive lab assignments.

- Collaborative groups are expected to communicate who will submit the assignment, when the assignment will be submitted, and how progress will be confirmed with all participating group members.
- Setting expectations for every member of the group will improve the likelihood that a complete assignment will be submitted.
- Each student may serve as the one designated to make the assignment submission no more than two times for each group configuration.
- Lab partners failing to participate and contribute to the satisfaction of all group members will not receive credit for the lab assignment.

Lab Quizzes (12 total, 5 points each):

At the end of every lab there will be an **individual** assessment of your knowledge related to the topics introduced in lecture and implemented in the most recent assignments. Knowledge of course standards and good programming practices will be evaluated throughout the semester.

- The best way to prepare for lab quizzes is to actively participate with your team during the lab session including contributing to both the written problems and the development of the programming problem solution.
- A lab quiz must be completed from the official location of your lab and without accessing any resources.

Exams (two midterms 100 points each, one final exam 150 points):

Exams will be **individual** assessments of your knowledge. Exams will consist of multiple-choice problems covering programming concepts, best programming practices, lab and homework assignments, and the interpretation of code.

Homework Assignments (7 total, 5 points each):

	Homework Assignment	Due at 11pm on
The homework assignments are **individual** efforts designed to give you the opportunity to solve problems on your own **without the assistance of other students**.	1	January 22
	2	February 5
	3	February 19
All assignments will be posted on Blackboard 10-14 days before they are due.	4	March 5
	5	March 26
Please review the course policies as they relate to **academic integrity** found later in this document.	6	April 9
	7	April 23

Lecture Quizzes (60 points possible):

At every meeting of lecture, starting with the second week of the term, a lecture quiz will take place. Quizzes may occur at the start of lecture, in the middle, and/or at the end of lecture.

iClicker response pads are **required** to participate in lecture quizzes. You should bring your response pad to every lecture. Your iClicker **must be registered by visiting the course Blackboard** site. Consult the ITaP Customer Service Center in the HSSE library (main floor) if you cannot read your serial number. Should your pad fail, or if you forget your pad, you may submit a written quiz using the form found in the back of your notes packet. You may only utilize this method once during the semester. **Only the form provided in the course notes packet will be accepted and must be submitted at the end of the current lecture for which it will be used.**

- Please review the **academic integrity policies** regarding the misrepresentation of identity as it relates to participating in a lecture quiz for another student.

Expectations for Lecture and Lab Meetings

Lectures

- You are expected to arrive to lecture on time and to remain on-task.
- Disruptive students will be excused from lecture and asked to meet with course staff before returning to class.
- Please silence all electronic devices during lecture.
- Lecture seats will be assigned by group so that you are seated next to your current lab partners. Check Blackboard Learn for your seat assignment. **Students not in their assigned seat will not receive credit for lecture quizzes.**

Labs

CS 159 labs will meet weekly (see lab schedule). You are expected to attend and to participate in every lab this semester. All lab assignments will be completed in collaborative teams assigned by your lab instructor. Lab assignments will be due 30 minutes before the start of your next lab and may require your team meet outside of class to complete the program.

- Groups are expected to communicate regarding the progress, completion, and submission of each lab programming assignment. Only the effort designated on the lab communication form and properly submitted by the group will be considered for grading.

Because of our use of teaming, **no points will be given to a student who is absent from, or late arriving to, a lab**. If you are going to have a regular conflict with your lab time, please change sections.

- At every lab meeting you will sign into the `guru` server and run the `attend` command. This will be the official recording of attendance.

- In addition to being on-time you must remain **an active participant** as you are expected to function as part of a team. Students that are off task during lab will be counted as absent.

- **Any student missing more than two labs (unexcused) will receive a failing grade for the course.**

Grading:

Assignment	Points
Homework	35
Lab Tasks	60
Midterm Exams	200
Final Exam	150
Lecture Quizzes	60
Lab Quizzes	60
Total Possible:	565

Grades:

Grade	Points Required
A	480
B	425
C	370
D	315

An equivalent number of points to earn a C are needed to receive a Pass if taking the course Pass/No Pass. It is recommended that graduate students in the course elect this option (see your advisor).

- The instructor reserves the right to lower the minimum score required for each letter grade. If such a move is made it will not be announced until **after the final exam**.
- At no time during the semester will it be speculated if this will be done or how much any given cutoff will be lowered. You should have no expectation that all cutoffs if moved will be moved by an equal amount.
- The use of plus (+) and minus (-) additions to a grade will be considered for those individual who are very close to, but fall short of, one of the posted minimum scores.

Our expectation of your lab instructor is that he/she grades your assignment in a **timely manner and provides you with adequate feedback** for improvement. If you feel this is not the case please address your concern to your lab instructor and the lecturer of the course. Typically, your lab instructor should be returning assignments 4-6 days after a given assignment is due.

Re-grade Request Policy:

To request a re-grade on any assignment you must make your **request in writing to the instructor's office (HAAS G-26)**. You have five days to appeal any grade from the day the assignment is returned to you. After that period the grades are frozen and no appeal will be considered.

A re-grade request must include the following:

1. A printed copy of the original graded assignment that was returned to you (if applicable).
2. An attached reason why you believe a re-grade is warranted.

- **Note:** A re-grade is not a second chance to complete an assignment. It is not a means to challenge assignment requirements, course policies, or programming and documentation standards.

Absences:

Only **documented and serious hardships** will be considered for any missed work.

If you have documentation of what you consider to be such a hardship then you must contact the lecturer in a timely manner **during office hours when you are able to resume participating in class**. Any student who knows in advance of an absence must make a request for consideration one week prior to the planned absence.

- University policies on absence and absence reporting are available from the Office of the Dean of Students: http://www.purdue.edu/studentregulations/regulations_procedures/classes.html
- Do not expect assignment deadlines or exam dates to be altered for reason of personal travel.
- Make-up requests for **reasons of illness MUST be accompanied by documentation from a medical professional** stating the dates you were under their care and the date you were cleared to return to school/work.

Important Assignment Guidelines:

All assignments must comply with **the programming and documentation standards of the course.** Programs that execute **and** meet minimum assignment requirements but are not logically correct or complete may be considered for partial credit.

To receive full credit, your program must (1) produce correct results, (2) be well-designed, (3) make efficient use of the limited resources of the computer, (4) follow assignment requirements, and (5) adhere to course programming and documentation standards.

An assignment that is not submitted as expected cannot be considered for a grade. Only work submitted correctly prior to the assignment deadline can be considered for grading. **Late work is not accepted.**

Demand for resources and course staff will increase as an assignment deadline nears. Waiting until the last minute to work on your programming assignments is discouraged! Course policy is **NOT to extend** deadlines unless campus resources (not your local ISP) are unavailable for an extended period near the deadline for an assignment.

You are responsible for understanding how to use the technology utilized by the course, this includes but is not limited to UNIX and related course tools such as the assignment submission script.

Be sure your account is set-up correctly as introduced during the first lab meeting of the semester.

Plan to submit work early! Allow sufficient time to seek assistance should you experience any difficulties with assignments or submitting an assignment.

Academic Integrity:

A very detailed set of criteria that is enforced rigorously related to academic integrity is applicable to CS 159. The consequences for violating course policies are serious.

You are encouraged to discuss any CS 159 topic including high-level ideas about how to approach an assignment. But, under **no circumstances will exchange of, or shared access to, code via written or electronic means be permitted** between teams for collaborative assignments or individuals for individual assignments.

It is considered dishonest either to read another team's solution or to provide anyone with access to your work (or that of another student). Be mindful when working on code with others on individual assignments as this is discouraged. The work you submit must be your own original effort and not the result of unacceptable, even if unintentional, collaboration.

Why enforce academic integrity? Academic integrity violations amount to theft. Theft of the work of the individual who developed the solution, theft of that individual's time, and theft of the instructor's time to conduct an inquiry into such matters. It amounts to **theft from every student** who has come to Purdue University, made a significant financial investment in their education, and has the expectation that their degree will be valued by employers and other academic institutions.

When is it no longer acceptable to discuss an assignment with another student or someone not from my group?

- Discussions with peers are most appropriate during the early phases of solution development. Once you begin to design and implement (write code) your solution you should be referencing course staff members exclusively for assistance.
- Working closely with another student on a homework assignment may result in highly similar work due to collaboration. Collaboration may not have been the intended approach to solving the problem but the end result of working closely with others for extended periods of time.

Every student is responsible for protecting their own work. Do not make the assumption that roommates, neighbors, significant others, or other **"trusted"** individuals would not take advantage of knowing your password, having access to your computer (use a password protected screen saver, log out when done), or taking a picture of your work when left on an unattended machine. **You are responsible for such events that leave your work unprotected.**

Many free on-line compilers or file depositories will store your work and leave it publicly visible unless you pay for their upgraded services. Please understand the policies of any such service before you make use of them. See the note above regarding your responsibility to protect your work.

Do not make the mistake of thinking that **superficial changes in a program** (such as altering comments, changing variable names, interchanging statements, or additional white spaces) will avoid detection. If you are unable to complete the work yourself, it is unlikely that you will succeed in disguising the work of another as your own. We are adamant that **violations in any form will not be tolerated**. Even the most trivial assignment is better not done than if you violate course integrity policies to complete it.

As easy as it is to share an electronic copy of a file, to gain access to a file through account sharing, sharing a hard copy of your work, or seeking assistance from strangers on the Internet, it is as just as easy to analyze and detect such sharing as it results in similar efforts being submitted.

Internet forums, including premium sites that advertise assistance in college courses, are monitored by course staff members. Any relevant code found is included with student submissions to test for similarity. Searching for and using solutions to assignments, requesting assistance on assignments, and the posting of assignments in a venue such as these is a violation of course academic integrity policies and potentially violations of University copyright.

Assume that every final submission you make during the semester will be analyzed by at least one software similarity service. These services will measure the percentage of similarity between your solution and those submitted by others in the course. Additionally, these services indicate the number of lines matched among submissions. **You will be solving problems this semester that have no unique solution and your solution is expected to be uniquely yours.** Concerns regarding any of our policies should be addressed during office hours prior to the deadline of an assignment.

Minimum consequences for violating course policies will include:

- First offense, a **zero for the assignment**, a **reduction of one letter grade at the end of the semester**, AND a **referral to the Office of the Dean of Students** for disciplinary action.
- Second offense, a zero for the assignment, a **failing grade for the course**, AND a referral to the Office of the Dean of Students for disciplinary action.

Notable exceptions to the first offense minimum consequences:

- Any violation on an exam will result in a failing grade for the course and a Dean of Students referral.
- Acts such as a misrepresentation of identity (or location) will result in a failing grade for the course and a Dean of Students referral. **This includes participating in a quiz for another student.**
- Posting to, requesting from, or accessing solutions found on unapproved sources, particularly those found on-line, will result in a failing grade for the course and a Dean of Students referral.

Collaborative Learning/Teaming/Participating as a Member of a Technical Team:

Here are our expectations of you and your group:

1. **Make time to meet with your group regularly.** There are 168 hours in a week, finding some common time for two or three people to meet should not be difficult. It is acceptable for just part of the group to meet some of the time if everyone cannot attend each meeting. It is the responsibility of each individual to plan their contribution to the group effort accordingly.
   - A group may exclude the name of a member from the lab assignment as a means of indicating a lack of satisfactory contribution to the group effort.

2. **Allow everyone an opportunity to express their ideas** on how to approach an assignment. One benefit of collaborative teaming is that everyone brings a different set of skills to the group and the resulting effort often is a stronger one than if it was completed individually.
   - When a group member becomes unresponsive to requests to meet or fails to update the other members of the group then those contributing members must continue without unresponsive member.

Collaborative Learning/Teaming/Participating as a Member of a Technical Team (continued):

3. **All group members must be satisfied with the final submission.** It is not acceptable for a group to submit an assignment that is not approved by all group members. "It is good enough" may be true for you but it is unfair for the others in the group who aspire for the highest grade possible.
   - ○ Likewise, each group member must be satisfied with your contribution to the group effort.

4. **Each group member must fully understand the entire assignment submitted.** Do not start your group meetings by trying to delegate the tasks to the different group members. Everyone must understand and contribute to every aspect of the assignment and its development.
   - ○ Assignments are an opportunity for you to demonstrate your knowledge of the programming concepts being utilized. Additionally, an assignment can be used to serve as a measure of what you don't know.

5. **Designate who will turn in the assignment, when it will be turned in, and how successful submission will be communicated with the rest of the group.** Only one person from the group will submit the assignment. Set a goal to submit the assignment well in advance of the due date to avoid any last minute problems related to group communication.
   - ○ **All groups are encouraged to exchange** that work which was developed in lab before leaving. This can be accomplished by making a submission with the Purdue e-mail address of each group member in the assignment header. Should a group member be unresponsive outside of class the remaining group members can proceed without starting over.

6. **You will work with the group assigned.** There is no other option in this course. Please see us with concerns you may have with your group. Take a professional approach with your group experience as similar to what you may experience at an internship or co-op experience.
   - ○ Groups will be re-assigned after every four labs.
   - ○ Future group assignments may take into consideration lecture attendance and assignment completion as an indicator of your interest in participating in the course. Active students in the course should not be burdened with partners who are not willing to stay current with course content.

Teaming experience is important to employers! Consider how your experience on a technical team in the lab might help you answer the following common questions asked in interviews:

- Tell me about a well-functioning team that you were on. Why do you think the team worked so well together?
- What actions and support, in your experience, make a team function successfully?
- Have you been a member of a team that struggled or failed? What assessment did you make of the reasons for the failure?
- Give me an example of a time when you had to teach a skill to other engineers.
- Some of the best ideas are born out of an individual's ability to challenge others' ways of thinking. Tell me about a time when you were successful doing this.
- For what assistance do fellow team members turn to you?

CS 159 Lab Schedule

All assignments due 30 minutes before the next lab begins.

Week of	Lab Assignment
January 8	**Account Set-Up Exercises**
January 15	Lab #1
January 22	Lab #2
January 29	Lab #3
February 5	Lab #4
February 12	Lab #5
February 19	Lab #6
February 26	Lab #7
March 5	**OPEN***
March 12	**SPRING BREAK**
March 19	Lab #8
March 26	Lab #9
April 2	Lab #10
April 9	Lab #11
April 16	Lab #12
April 23	**OPEN***
April 30	**FINALS WEEK**

* Labs will NOT meet during OPEN weeks unless warranted by an extenuating circumstance.

CS 159 Lecture Schedule

Week of	Lecture Topic
January 8	Introduction – UNIX and course tools
January 15	Chapter 2
January 22	Chapter 3
January 29	Chapter 4
February 5	Chapter 4
February 12	Chapter 5
February 19	Chapter 5
February 26	Chapter 6
March 5	Chapter 6*
March 12	**Spring Break**
March 19	Chapter 6
March 26	MATLAB File I/O*
April 2	Chapter 8
April 9	Chapter 8
April 16	Chapter 11
April 23	Chapters 9 & 10
April 30	**FINALS WEEK**

- **Note:** Lecture will not meet on Thursday March 8th or Thursday March 29th to compensate for the two midterm evening exams.

Course Syllabus Subject to Change with Notice

COURSE PROGRAMMING AND DOCUMENTATION STANDARDS

Programming Standards – How we expect you to approach the development of your solution. Includes our definitions of what are good programming practices and what we consider to be bad practices.

Documentation Standards – How we want your code to be formatted and documented when submitted.

Please read and revisit the section carefully throughout the semester.

Documentation, Programming, and Course Standards

Grading Standards

Every assignment will attempt to provide sufficient detail on all requirements. However, because the problems solved in this class have no unique solution, we will rely on the general guidelines listed below when determining the appropriate evaluation of your work.

You will always be evaluated on the following aspects of your assignments:

1. Following provided assignment **requirements**.
2. Developing the appropriate logic to solve the problem, accepting input in the order expected, and **producing expected output**.
3. Implementation of **good programming practices**.
4. Your solution should be **efficiently designed** to minimize abuse of the limited resources of the computer.
5. Abiding by **course documentation standards**.

It is possible to receive less than full-credit for an assignment if each of the above is not followed to course expectations. Aspects of your submission other than the generation of correct output are important and can result in a loss of significant points on an assignment.

Documentation Standards

The requirement of good documentation practices is universal among professionals; the primary motivation of having documentation standards is to make your code and logic as easy to understand and for your grader to evaluate as possible. The solutions you are in the process of developing must be easily interpreted when seeking assistance both in this class and from your colleagues and supervisors in the future.

These standards are not merely recommendations they are required for the course and failure to comply will result in a loss of points.

- The course notes and examples in lecture will attempt to abide by these standards as closely as possible to serve as an example. However, to save space in the notes and time during lecture, headers and comments may be excluded; this is not an option for your assignments.
- Various references, including the required textbook, do not abide by all of our standards; please refer to this document for clarification.

Points on an assignment will be deducted if your code and/or logic is difficult for your grader to evaluate because it fails to meet the expectations outlined in this document.

Is there real world relevance for programming standards? Most companies have extensive documentation requirements in order to facilitate the transfer of previously developed code from one employee to another without the need to spend a great deal of time trying to comprehend the work of the original developer.

Assignment Headers

- Assignment headers are used in the course to explain who the author/s is/are and provides a detailed description of the logic being implemented in a program or user-defined function.
- There are four total headers we will use this semester. Two for labs, one for homework, and another for user-defined functions within C assignments. One is for the Octave/MATLAB assignment and the remaining three for C assignments.
- The use of a header MUST NOT interfere with the compilation, execution, or submission of your program.

Lab Header Example (for C programs)

```
/*************************************************************************
 *
 *   Programmers and Purdue Email Addresses:
 *   1. login1@purdue.edu
 *   2. login2@purdue.edu
 *   3. login3@purdue.edu (delete line if no third partner)
 *
 *   Lab #:
 *
 *   Academic Integrity Statement:
 *
 *   We have not used source code obtained from any other unauthorized source,
 *   either modified or unmodified.  Neither have we provided access to our code
 *   to another. The project we are submitting is our own original work.
 *
 *   Day, Time, Location of Lab:
 *
 *   Program Description:
 *
 *************************************************************************/
```

- Be sure to list the Purdue e-mail address for each participating group member! Grades are collected and uploaded to Blackboard based on your Purdue career account.
  - You **MUST** delete any extra `login1`, `login2`, `login3` addresses before attempting a submission.
- After each submission of a lab assignment the members of the group who are correctly identified in the lab header by their Purdue e-mail address will receive a confirmation e-mail.

Homework Header (for C programs)

```
/*************************************************************************
 *
 *   Programmer and Purdue Email Address:
 *   1. login@purdue.edu
 *
 *   Homework #:
 *
 *   Academic Integrity Statement:
 *
 *   I have not used source code obtained from any other unauthorized source,
 *   either modified or unmodified.  Neither have I provided access to my code
 *   to another. The project I am submitting is my own original work.
 *
 *   Day, Time, Location of Lab:
 *
 *   Program Description:
 *
 *************************************************************************/
```

Be sure each of the following are correct in your lab and homework assignment headers:

- For lab headers use the full name of every student in your group. **Failing to include the official university email address of a group member will result in no credit being assigned to these individuals.**
- The academic integrity statement will be provided for you and MUST remain in the lab and homework header. Do not make any changes to the integrity statement.
- **A verbose program description is necessary.** If your lab instructor is unable to follow your logic after a quick glance at your code then they should be able to determine from your description the algorithm you were attempting to implement. A verbose program description will mean fewer necessary comments within the code of your program.
- The lab division and section can be the **day, time, and location** of your weekly lab meeting.

Function Header (for C programs)

```
/*****************************************************************
 *
 *   Function Information
 *
 *   Name of Function:
 *
 *   Function Return Type:
 *
 *   Parameters (list data type, name, and comment one per line):
 *     1.
 *     2.
 *     3.
 *
 *   Function Description:
 *
 *****************************************************************/
```

- With functions, it is important to comment your parameters (those values received by a function) in the header! There is no room to comment parameters in the first line of the function definition and it must be included here.

Object Names / Identifiers

- We will consider the following to be objects in this course: **variables, functions, symbolic/defined constants.** You must **give your objects names that reflect their purpose in the program**.

```
int x;
int y;                              Course Standard: Declare only one variable per line!
int z;
```

- Can you determine what the variables x, y, and z accomplish for the program based only on the name of the variable? Perhaps they hold information on a 3D point? If the program contains no 3D coordinate data, then the use of x, y, and z as variable names is unclear.
- **Rarely is a single character identifier for an object meaningful**. A reasonable exception would be for a loop control variable used for simple counting or to access the elements of the array.
- The use of the underscore to begin an identifier is not a practice that we will use in the course.

```
int numStudents;        Relevant variable, constant, and function names assist in the documentation, and
float objectMass;       readability, of the logic you are attempting to implement.
char courseGrade;
```

Variable Initialization

```
int numStudents = 0;                                    //OKAY TO KEEP HERE
float objectMass = calcMass(acceleration, velocity);    //MOVE TO EXECUTABLES
```

- In general it is acceptable to initialize a variable declared in the local declaration section of a user-defined function. If the expression used to initialize the variable is more complex than a constant assignment then it is best to give the variable its first value inside of the executable statement section of the function.

15

Symbolic/Defined Constants

- THE SELECTION OF IDENTIFIERS FOR SYMBOLIC/DEFINED CONSTANTS MUST BE IN ALL CAPS.
- This standard allows any programmer to differentiate between a variable, a function call, and a constant in an expression.
- Define all symbolic/defined constants at the top of your program immediately following the assignment header.
- Because the use of symbolic/defined constants can improve the documentation of a program it is a standard of the course that you attempt to maximize your use of symbolic/defined constants and minimize your use of literal constants (see chapter 3).

> **Note: Memory constants will not be used in this course.**

Commenting

In the C programming language we have two possible implementations of comments:

- The single line comment // that will instruct the compiler to ignore everything after // to the end of the line.
- The multi-line comment /* */ that will instruct the compiler to ignore everything between the /* and */. See the headers above for an example of this type of comment.
  - Multi-line comments cannot be nested in the C language.
- MATLAB utilizes % for a single line comment and %{ and %} for a multi-line comment.

What **must** be commented?

- **EVERY variable** that you declare must have a brief comment to describe its purpose in the program!
  - In C, comment variables to the right of where they are declared.
  - In MATLAB, list and comment all variables in the relevant course assignment header.
- Within a given function it is expected that the occasional complex segment of code be documented in order to inform others regarding that logic you are attempting to implement.
  - For example: It is recommended that you place a line or two of comments before any significant selection or repetition construct.

Indenting

You must indent all code inside the body of a structure **two (additional) spaces**! Rarely should you ever begin a line of code in the first column of your editor! Here are some common structures properly indented according to our standards:

```
if(x == 3 || y == 2)
{
  z++;
  a = a - 1;
}
```

```
do
{
  e = m * c * c;
  avg = sum/number;
}while(r == 0);
```

```
for(x = 1; x <= MAX; x++)
{
  printf("%d", x);
}
```

Nested structure demonstrated:

```
if(y == 3)
{
  for(g = 0; g > MIN; g--)
  {
    y = y - g;
  }
}
```

More Indenting Examples:

Correct	Incorrect	Also Incorrect

```if(x == 3 || y == 2)```
```{```
``` z++;```
``` a = a - 1;```
```}```
	```if(x == 3 || y == 2)```
	``` {```
	``` z++;```
	``` a = a - 1;```
	``` }```
		```if(x == 3 || y == 2){```
		``` z++;```
		``` a = a - 1;```
		```}```

Switch constructs will be indented as seen in the C text! See page 258.		

White-Spacing

- Please place an additional line between sections to help "group" the code
- Balance the use of additional lines and failing to place any throughout your code.
  - There is no need to double space all lines of code.
- It is a requirement to **place a space between operators and operands**, such as: `y = y - g;`
- In MATLAB do not use the command `clc` to clear the screen.

Programming Standards

There are numerous reasons for programming standards; in this course the purpose of such standards as described here is to help you develop good habits for your future programming endeavors. For some of you, this requirement will require breaking previously developed bad habits.

What makes a habit bad? If a few of the implementations discussed below are not used properly they can expose your program to difficult errors for a beginner to debug, program crashes, hacking, or represent programming language features that are anticipated to be obsolete in the future.

Keep Local Declarations Separate from Executable Statements

- The current version of the `gcc` compiler may permit variable definitions anywhere in a function. This interpretation by the compiler does not follow the historical standard for the C programming language that all variables are declared prior to the start of the executable statements.
    - See Figure 2-2 in Chapter 2 of C text for more information.

Scope

- VARIABLES ARE **NEVER** PERMITTED TO HAVE GLOBAL SCOPE.
- Do you need to share a variable with another function? Do you need a variable value to change within a function and to retain that change after the function terminates?
    - You must understand how to pass the variables/values to and return them from a user-defined function.
    - We reserve the right to assign a **score of zero** for the implementation of global variables.
- We expect in this course that all function declarations will have a global scope.
- Do not reuse an identifier with two objects that have overlapping scope.

Symbolic/Defined Constants and other Pre-processor Directives

- All pre-processor directives must go at the top of your program just below the appropriate assignment header of the file.
- You can read much more about symbolic/defined constants in your C text (appendix G) but one purpose of a symbolic/defined constant is to make your role as programmer easier when the requirements for a program are modified in the future.

The use of { and }

- You may observe in the C programming text that it is possible in certain situations to omit the braces around the body of structures such as `if`, `for`, and `while`.
    - Do not develop or continue this habit! Beginners have a difficult enough time pairing up their braces and a misplaced brace is one of the more difficult errors to resolve.
- We will discuss the **dangling** `else` problem in chapter 5 (page 245 of the C text, figure 5-14) as an example of one difficult logical error to debug when you omit the braces as we have required. You will also encounter the book's lack of { and } when you try to make sense of the sorting algorithms coded in chapter 8 of the text.

> **For all relevant selection and repetition constructs in C the use of { and } is required.**

- MATLAB/Octave does not make use of { and } to delimit structures such as functions, selection, and repetition. It is recommended that you appropriately indent, make use of ; when reasonable, and correctly implement the `end` statement to format your MATLAB/Octave code.

Proper Use of Repetition

- Use `for` loops only with counter-controlled processes.
- Make use of all three expressions with every `for` loop. Do not leave expressions empty or place meaningless statements in any of the expressions such as `x = x`.
- The use of the comma operator is probably unnecessary in `for` loops for this class. See page 323 of the C text.
- The use of perpetual loops would violate the expectation that control-forcing statements are prohibited.
  - See next section.
- Recursion must only be used with counter-controlled processes.

Control Forcing Statements

- **You may observe control forcing statements being used in the texts but their use is prohibited within the course.** Often there are better ways to dictate the control of your program without using one of the following statements:
  - `exit`, `goto`, `break` (permitted only with `switch` structures in C), `continue`
  - **Multiple `return` statements in the same function.** A function, much like the flowcharts we will discuss in lecture, must have only one starting and ending point. Using multiple `return` statements enables multiple ending points for a single function (algorithm).

Standard Libraries and Functions

- You are permitted to use many of the functions in the standard C libraries introduced in class. **It is your responsibility** for asking a course staff member about a function or library we have not discussed in class that you would like to use.

User-Defined Functions

Once we introduce Functions (chapter 4) only the following will be permitted in the `main` function of a program:

1. Declaration of those variables that need to be passed between functions.
   - All variables in the function definition should have an explicit data type.
2. Functions called by `main`.
3. A minimum amount of control code (loops, selection) to maintain `main` as the control center of the program.

The `main` function is intended to be *the main function* of the program and a majority of the function calls should originate in `main`. Most of the data defined in the program should be done in `main`.

According to the definition of a function, each function must only have an individual (single) specific task. Failing to make good use of user-defined functions on relevant assignments will result in no partial credit.

For further discussion on user-defined functions read the following sections of your text:

- **Chapter 4.8 Structure Charts**
- **Pay particular attention to the section on functional cohesion on page 211.**

Passing individual values by address should meet the following criteria:

1. When more than one value needs to be revised and that revision be retained in the calling function once the called function terminates.
2. The function continues to meet the definition of being **functionally cohesive** such that it completes only a single fundamental task.

Declaration of Arrays

All arrays will be **static** (of fixed-length) until we introduce the topic of **dynamic** memory allocation in chapters 9 and 10 of the C programming text. The application of variable-length arrays as seen in the example on pages 478 – 479 **will violate course standards** as it permits the local declarations and executable statements in a function to overlap.

- **It is unacceptable to make use of a variable to represent the size of an array in an array declaration.**
- **A symbolic/defined constant will be used when declaring arrays.**

Advance Topics/Implementations

- In course assignments we will state from which chapters you may reference when developing your solution.
- We commonly view advance implementations (material not covered yet in lecture) in code as suspicious in that we consider such an implementation to be beyond what most students in the course are capable of and suspect that the author of the code may be someone not currently in the class.

Efficient Design

- One measure regarding the quality of ALL assignments is the implementation of efficient design. Engineering students should anticipate and appreciate that design is critical to the evaluation of any product including software.
- We require that you implement an efficient and logically correct algorithm as part of your assignment. In some cases this may make the distinction between letter grades on the assignment. To receive full credit on an assignment we expect **correct logic AND good design**.

Some guidelines related to the efficient use of the limited resources of the computer:

- Avoid wasting memory.
  - Do not use multiple arrays (or dimensions) when one will do the job.
  - Do not declare (in C) arrays to be large beyond your data needs (specified by the assignment).
  - Do not use arrays when they are unnecessary.

- Avoid wasting the CPU's time.
  - Do not write nested loops for tasks that can be done in one (or none).

- Shorter code is usually better. Recognize patterns in your code. Avoid duplication of the same logic within a program.
  - If you find yourself repeating code in several places, create a function such that the code only appears once in your program and is called when needed.
  - Another common scenario involves several functions have been written that do essentially the same thing, or contain a considerable amount of similar code. In such cases you should attempt to consolidate as much as possible.

- Use the top-down design. Each function should have a well-defined task and not a series of tasks.

- Topics of efficient design will be commented on, where appropriate, in lecture.

Syntax Errors and Warnings

- Any assignment submitted with a **syntax error** will receive **no consideration for partial-credit**.
  - You are responsible for testing your work thoroughly prior to submission.

- Compiler warnings will result in a loss of points and should be remedied prior to submission of your final effort.

UNIX and Windows (or other operating systems)

1. We DO NOT encourage that you develop, compile, or to test your code in ANY editor or compiler other than those introduced in this course. Not all C compilers or versions of MATLAB/Octave are fully compatible. You should want to test your work under the same conditions that it will be processed and tested by the course.
2. It is your responsibility to thoroughly test your code on the `gcc` compiler on `guru.itap.purdue.edu` as set up during the first week of the semester prior to submitting your work! For MATLAB assignments test your work on `guru.itap.purdue.edu` with Octave, a program mostly compatible with MATLAB.
3. **We will not support compilers,** editors, and shells **other than the default** `gcc` **compiler on ITaP's** `guru` machine, `vi`, and `csh`. **All students must be sure to set your host machine to:** `guru.itap.purdue.edu`

The use of other editors may result in formatting which appears differently to your lab instructor than how it appears to you when opened in the original editor. Much of this has to do with how white space characters such as tabs are interpreted. You are responsible for verifying that any editor treats white space the same way as `vi` on `guru`.

Verifying a Successful Submission

How do you know if your assignment has been submitted as expected?

- Collaborative assignments such as labs are e-mailed to each member of the group based on the Purdue University e-mail addresses listed in the assignment header upon a successful submission.
  - ○ Consider making a submission prior to leaving a lab session so that each of the group members has a copy of all work created during lab.
- Individual homework assignments are e-mailed only to the submitter upon a successful submission.
  - ○ It is your responsibility to review the e-mail sent to verify you have submitted the correct file, to the correct lab section, and to the correct assignment.
- **Are you not receiving confirmation e-mails?**
  - ○ If your Purdue University e-mail is forwarded to an off campus service then you'll need to check your SPAM or JUNK folders. Many such services will think such mail is unsolicited given how it is formatted and how frequently messages are sent.

You are advised to leave sufficient time prior to the assignment deadline to seek assistance should you encounter a difficulty with assignment submission. No late work will be accepted.

Old Exam and Solutions

Exam #1:

1. A	2. B	3. D	4. A	5. C
6. B	7. A	8. A	9. C	10. A
11. A	12. B	13. C	14. B	15. C
16. C	17. B	18. C	19. C	20. B
21. C	22. C	23. C	24. C	25. C
26. A	27. B	28. B	29. B	30. A
31. B	32. B	33. C	34. A	35. D

Exam #2:

1. C	2. B	3. D	4. A	5. D
6. A	7. B	8. A	9. C	10. A
11. A	12. C	13. B	14. C	15. A
16. B	17. A	18. A	19. D	20. C
21. B	22. A	23. C	24. D	25. C
26. D	27. B	28. A	29. B	30. A
31. C	32. B	33. A	34. C	35. A

Final Exam:

1. C	2. A	3. B	4. B	5. A
6. C	7. A	8. C	9. A	10. A
11. C	12. B	13. A	14. B	15. B
16. B	17. C	18. D	19. C	20. A
21. B	22. A	23. C	24. C	25. B
26. B	27. C	28. C	29. D	30. B
31. C	32. C	33. B	34. C	35. B
36. C	37. D	38. B	39. A	40. C
41. A	42. C	43. C	44. B	45. A
46. D	47. B	48. D	49. C	

How are old exams best used in the process of preparing for an exam?

- At the end of your studying you should attempt an old exam and do so at a location on campus that will allow you to simulate the exam environment. Take the exam, grade your work, and identify what subjects or types of problems need further review prior to the exam date.

Where can I find more problems for practice?

- See the problems at the end of each chapter in the C programming text.

- A link to the publisher's site which includes student downloads and solutions is available on Blackboard.

Why is some of the code so complex in these old exams?

- Every exam is specific to the semester it was given. This not only includes the topics covered based on when the exam took place, but also the assignments that have been given in the course that semester.

- Many code segments are directly from previous homework and lab programming concepts and those students would have some level of familiarity with the problem and logic being presented. This would make interpreting the code and the logic it represents easier and faster.

CS 159 Midterm Exam #1
Tuesday October 2, 2017 [8:00pm – 9:00pm] – Elliott Hall of Music
Instructor: William Crum
35 Questions * 3 Points Each = 105 Points
Any points earned beyond 100 are considered extra credit.

Exam Rules/Notices:

1. Complete your name and your student ID number on the answer sheet (write in AND bubble-in all requested information). There is no exam form or section to indicate on your answer sheet.
   - **An incorrect student ID number will result in a zero for this exam.** All student ID numbers begin with two zero digits. This must be written and "bubbled in" on your exam answer sheet.
   - **You must be in your assigned seat to receive credit for this exam.**

2. Make sure you have all 35 questions to this exam. You should answer every question. All questions only have one best answer. Please be careful when filling in your answers, any answer determined to be unreadable by Instructional Data Processing will be considered incorrect. Only the answer on your answer sheet can be considered when grading.
   - An **ASCII table** and **operator precedence table** have been provided on the back of this exam.

3. **NO QUESTIONS WILL BE ANSWERED DURING THE EXAM.** We do not answer questions during the exam due to the limited number of staff members present. It is easier for us to compensate for an erroneous test question than it is to answer questions or to effectively make an announcement during the examination period.
   - **Manage your time accordingly!**

4. You must assume that all C programs and code segments are implemented on the `guru.itap` machine and would be compiled with the `gcc` compiler as set up during the first week of the semester. When segments of code are presented you may assume that the appropriate include statements are present and that the code would be inside of a fully operational function or program.

5. **Protect your work and keep your focus on your own exam.** It is considered dishonest if you copy from another student or to permit another student to copy from you. Anyone found to violate course policies will receive a **failing grade for the course** and will be referred to the Office of the Dean of Students.

6. **You are NOT permitted to use any resources during this exam.** This includes but is not limited to; **texts, notes, calculators, cell phones, audio devices, and computers**. If your cell phone audibly rings during the exam you will be required to immediately submit your exam and leave the testing facility.

7. When you are finished with the exam, please proceed to the lobby to submit your answer form and to exit the facility. **You will be required to show photo identification before we can accept your work.** You will keep this exam form. You may not return to your seat once you have submitted your exam.

8. Scores and official exam answers will appear on Blackboard no later than Friday (October 6). Do not contact course staff members about mistakes (if any) until answers are posted. If you feel an error remains after answers have been posted you may make a written request for a regrade by Thursday October 12 and deliver it to HAAS G-26 (you may slide it under the door outside of office hours). Your request must be a hard copy (no e-mail) and include a detailed description, using code if applicable, demonstrating your belief why the posted answer is incorrect.

9. **When time is called ALL writing must stop.** You are not permitted to continue to make revisions to any answer on your exam once time has been called.

10. Schedule reminders:
    - Lecture will not meet Thursday October 5. Lecture will resume after the break on Thursday October 12.
    - All lab sections meet this week. Lab will not meet Wednesday October 11 through Friday October 13.

NO QUESTIONS WILL BE ANSWERED DURING THE EXAM.

Use the program below for problem #1

```c
#include<stdio.h>
#include<math.h>

int main()
{
  int velocity_mph = 75;
  int distance_miles = 340;
  int time;

  int hours;
  int minutes;

  time = distance_miles / velocity_mph;

  hours = floor(time);

  minutes = time - (int)time;

  printf("Result time [%02d:%02d]\n", hours, minutes * 60);

  return(0);
}
```

1. Which of the following is the output generated by the code segment above?
   A. `Result time [04:00]`
   B. `Result time [4:32]`
   C. `Result time [04:32]`
   D. None of the above.

2. Which of the following statements is TRUE regarding the `printf` and `scanf` functions?
   A. A single `scanf` statement cannot be used to accept input for multiple variables.
   B. It is possible to format data output with left-alignment when using a `printf` statement.
   C. A `scanf` statement will return the value entered by the user of the program.
   D. None of the above.

3. Which of the following statements is FALSE regarding the selection of a data type for a variable?
   A. The data type of a variable will determine those operators with which it may be used.
   B. The data type which can be stored by a variable cannot be altered during the execution of the program.
   C. The data type of a variable will determine the amount of memory to reserve for the variable.
   D. None of the above.

4. Which of the following regarding placeholders in the `printf` function is FALSE?
   A. If the width modifier provided is too small for the data to be display then digits will be truncated so that the value fits in the number of spaces specified.
   B. The width modifier can be used with values in either the floating-point or integer family of data types.
   C. The size modifier to the conversion code is required with the longer numeric data types.
   D. None of the above.

Use the program below for problems #5 - #6

```c
#include<stdio.h>
#include<math.h>

#define PI 3.1

int main()
{
  float radius = 4;
  float length = 2;
  float surfArea;
  float volume;

  int modifier1;
  int modifier2;

  surfArea = (4 * PI * pow(radius, 2)) / 2 + (2 * radius) * length;
  volume = (PI * pow(radius, 2) * length) / 2;

  modifier1 = (int)(surfArea * 10) % 10;
  modifier2 = (int)volume;

  printf("-=-=-=-=-=-=-=-=-=-=-=-=-\n");
  printf("Surface Area: %13.*f\n", modifier1 / 2, surfArea);
  printf("Volume: %*.2f\n", modifier2 / 3, volume);
  printf("-=-=-=-=-=-=-=-=-=-=-=-=-\n");

  return(0);
}
```

5. Which of the following are the first two lines of output generated by the program above?

```
-=-=-=-=-=-=-=-=-=-=-=-=-
Surface Area:         115.19
```
A

```
-=-=-=-=-=-=-=-=-=-=-=-=-
Surface Area:         115.20
```
B

```
-=-=-=-=-=-=-=-=-=-=-=-=-
Surface Area:         115.2
```
C

None of the above.   D

6. Which of the following are the final two lines of output generated by the program above?

```
Volume:              49.60
-=-=-=-=-=-=-=-=-=-=-=-=-
```
A

```
Volume:              49.60
-=-=-=-=-=-=-=-=-=-=-=-=-
```
B

```
Volume:              49.60
-=-=-=-=-=-=-=-=-=-=-=-=-
```
C

None of the above.   D

7. Given A and B are integer variables, both are greater than zero, and A is less than B. What is the range of values possible as a result of the expression: B % A?
   A. Range is [0, A - 1]
   B. Range is [0, A]
   C. Range is [0, B - 1]
   D. Range is [0, B]

27

```c
#include<stdio.h>

#define LEVEL1 100
#define LEVEL2 300

#define COST1 5 / 2
#define COST2 6
#define COST3 15 / 2

int determineLevel(int, int);
void printCost(int, int);

int main()
{
  int level = 1;
  int qty = 200;

  level += determineLevel(qty, LEVEL1);
  level += determineLevel(qty, LEVEL2);

  printCost(level, qty);

  level = 1 + determineLevel(310, LEVEL1);
  level += determineLevel(310, LEVEL2);

  printCost(level, 310);

  return(0);
}
void printCost(int x, int y)
{
  int cost;

  cost = (x / 1) * (1 / x) * COST1 * y;
  cost += (x / 2) * (2 / x) * COST2 * y;
  cost += (x / 3) * (3 / x) * COST3 * y;

  printf("Cost: %d\n", cost);
}

int determineLevel(int x, int y)
{
  return((x / y + 2) % (x / y + 1));
}
```

8. Which of the following is the first line of output generated by the program above?
   A. Cost: 1200
   B. Cost: 1400
   C. Cost: 2400
   D. None of the above.

9. Which of the following is the second line of output generated by the program above?
   A. Cost: 620
   B. Cost: 1860
   C. Cost: 2170
   D. None of the above.

```
int x = 7;
int y = 19;
float a = 10.5;
float b = 2;

printf("Result #1: %.1f\n", y / x * b);
printf("Result #2: %.1f\n", x / b * a);

b *= y / 3 + 1;

printf("Result #3: %.1f\n", b);
```

10. Which of the following is the output generated by the first print statement in the code segment above?
   - A. Result #1: 4.0
   - B. Result #1: 5.0
   - C. Result #1: 5.4
   - D. None of the above.

11. Which of the following is the output generated by the second print statement in the code segment above?
   - A. Result #2: 36.8
   - B. Result #2: 31.5
   - C. Result #2: 31.0
   - D. None of the above.

12. Which of the following is the output generated by the third print statement in the code segment above?
   - A. Result #3: 13.7
   - B. Result #3: 14.0
   - C. Result #3: 14.7
   - D. None of the above.

Use the program below for problem #13

```
#include<stdio.h>

void numberChanges(int, int*);

int main()
{
  int x = 25;
  int y = 15;

  numberChanges(y, &x);
  numberChanges(x, &y);

  printf("x: %d y: %d\n", x, y);

  return(0);
}

void numberChanges(int a, int *b)
{
  a = *b;
  *b = a;
}
```

13. Which of the following is the output generated by the program above?
   - A. x: 15 y: 15
   - B. x: 15 y: 25
   - C. x: 25 y: 15
   - D. None of the above.

```
#include<stdio.h>

int changeOne(int, int);

int main()
{
    int x = 5;
    int y = 4;

    x = changeOne(x, y++);

    printf("x: %d\n", x);

    y = changeOne(y + 1, y + 2);

    printf("y: %d\n", y);

    return(0);
}

int changeOne(int a, int b)
{
    b++;

    return(b / a + a);
}
```

14. Which of the following is the first line of output generated by the program above?
    A. x: 5
    B. x: 6
    C. x: 7
    D. None of the above.

15. Which of the following is the second line of output generated by the program above?
    A. y: 5
    B. y: 6
    C. y: 7
    D. None of the above.

16. Which of the following describes what it means for a user-defined function to be functionally cohesive?
    A. When a called function has parameters with the same identifiers as those in the calling function.
    B. When the called function has more than one parameter and all are of the same data type.
    C. When the called function accomplishes only a single task in the program.
    D. None of the above.

17. Which of the following regarding the use of passing parameters by address and standards of the course is TRUE?
    A. The use of pass by address is limited to void functions.
    B. The use of pass by address allows for multiple changes in the called function to be available back in the calling function.
    C. The use of pass by address permits the completion of multiple tasks per function.
    D. None of the above.

```c
int a = 7;
int b = 3;
int c = 12;
float result;

c += a++ + ++b;

printf("c: %d\n", c);

c = (float) a / b--;

printf("c: %.1f\n", (float) c);

c = 5.0;
result = (c + a) / b;

printf("result: %.1f\n", result);
```

18. Which of the following is the first line of output generated by the code segment above?
   A. c: 25
   B. c: 24
   C. c: 23
   D. None of the above.

19. Which of the following is the second line of output generated by the code segment above?
   A. c: 3.0
   B. c: 2.3
   C. c: 2.0
   D. None of the above.

20. Which of the following is the third line of output generated by the code segment above?
   A. result: 4.3
   B. result: 4.0
   C. result: 3.7
   D. None of the above.

Use the code segment below for problems #21 - #22

```c
int x = 21;
int y = 37;
int z = 5;

int result;

result = x % 2 && y % 2 && z % 2;
result += x / y || x / z;

printf("Result #1: %d\n", result);

result = x - y && y - z || z - x;
result += x + y / z || y - x / z * z && z / z - 1;

printf("Result #2: %d\n", result);
```

21. Which of the following is the first line of output generated by the code segment above?
   A. Result #1: 0
   B. Result #1: 1
   C. Result #1: 2
   D. None of the above.

22. Which of the following is the second line of output generated by the code segment above?
   A. Result #2: 0
   B. Result #2: 1
   C. Result #2: 2
   D. None of the above.

```c
#include<stdio.h>

int remainCount(int, int, int);

int main()
{
   int x = 5;
   int y = 10;
   int z = 15;

   int ct;

   ct = remainCount(x, y, z);
   ct += remainCount(y, z, x);
   ct += remainCount(z, x, y);

   printf("first count: %d\n", ct);

   ct = remainCount(x, z, remainCount(y, x, z));

   printf("second count: %d\n", ct);

   return(0);
}

int remainCount(int x, int y, int z)
{
   int result;

   result = x % y + x % z;

   return(result);
}
```

23. Which of the following is the first line of output generated by the code segment above?
   A. first count: 10
   B. first count: 15
   C. first count: 25
   D. None of the above.

24. Which of the following is the second line of output generated by the code segment above?
   A. second count: 0
   B. second count: 5
   C. second count: 10
   D. None of the above.

25. Which of the following regarding the control of a program and the use of user-defined functions is FALSE?
   A. All functions that return a value also return control of the program to the calling function upon terminating.
   B. The calling function will resume from the point of the function call once the called function terminates.
   C. Failing to use the keyword return in a void function will result in the control of the program returning to the main function which may not necessarily be the calling function.
   D. None of the above.

```c
#include<stdio.h>

int calcSum(int, int, int);
int calcProd(int, int);
int calcMod(int);

int main()
{
   int x = 11;
   int y = 5;
   int z = 8;

   printf("Result #1: %d\n", calcSum(x, y, z));
   printf("Result #2: %d\n", calcProd(x, y));
   printf("Result #3: %d\n", calcMod(1 - calcSum(y, z, x)));

   return(0);
}

int calcSum(int x, int y, int z)
{
   return(calcProd(x + y, z));
}

int calcProd(int x, int y)
{
   return(calcMod(x * y));
}

int calcMod(int x)
{
   return(x % 2);
}
```

26. Which of the following is the first line of output generated by the code segment above?
    A. Result #1: 0
    B. Result #1: 1
    C. Result #1: 24
    D. None of the above.

27. Which of the following is the second line of output generated by the code segment above?
    A. Result #2: 0
    B. Result #2: 1
    C. Result #2: 55
    D. None of the above.

28. Which of the following is the third line of output generated by the code segment above?
    A. Result #3: -1
    B. Result #3: 0
    C. Result #3: 1
    D. None of the above.

29. Which of the following CANNOT be determined by viewing the structure chart of a program?
    A. The order in which user-defined functions are called in a program.
    B. The number of times functions from the standard libraries (`stdio.h`, `math.h`) are used in a program.
    C. The calling function for each user-defined function in a program.
    D. None of the above.

30. Which of the following statements is TRUE regarding the use of comments according to the course standards or the rules of the C programming language?
    A. Parameters to a user-defined function are commented in the course function header.
    B. Multi-line comments can be nested, that is a multi-line comment can be found inside of another multi-line comment.
    C. When related variables are declared in the local declaration section of a function only the first one must be commented.
    D. None of the above.

31. Which of the following statements regarding expressions is FALSE?
    A. An expression always reduces to a single value.
    B. If multiple variables are modified once in an expression then the result is undefined.
    C. The left operand in an assignment expression must be a single variable.
    D. None of the above.

32. Which of the following statements regarding explicit data type conversions is FALSE?
    A. An assignment type conversion may result in a higher ranked data type being converted into a lower ranked data type.
    B. Explicit data type conversions can only be applied to variables and not to literal or symbolic/defined constants.
    C. The result of an explicit data type conversion may include the loss of data when a higher ranked data type is converted to a lower ranked data type.
    D. None of the above.

33. Which of the following statements regarding user-defined function parameters and local variables is FALSE?
    A. Parameters are defined in the first line of the function definition.
    B. Parameters in the function definition are initialized by the value they receive from the calling function.
    C. A variable declared in the local declaration section of a function can have the same identifier as one of the parameters of the same function.
    D. None of the above.

34. Which of the following statements regarding the first line of the function definition is TRUE?
    A. The first line of the function definition requires the data types and identifiers for each parameter.
    B. The first line of the function definition terminates with a semicolon (;).
    C. The first line of the function definition does not require an explicit return type for the function.
    D. None of the above.

35. Which of the following statements regarding this exam is TRUE?
    A. There is no form or section to indicate on your answer sheet.
    B. Lecture will not meet on Thursday October 5th.
    C. Lab will meet for the remainder of this week (October 4th - 7th) but will not meet next week following the break (October 11th – October 13th).
    D. ALL OF THE ABOVE.

ASCII Table

Char	Dec	Char	Dec	Char	Dec	Char	Dec
delimiter	0	space	32	@	64	`	96
(soh)	1	!	33	A	65	a	97
(stx)	2	"	34	B	66	b	98
(etx)	3	#	35	C	67	c	99
(eot)	4	$	36	D	68	d	100
(enq)	5	%	37	E	69	e	101
(ack)	6	&	38	F	70	f	102
(bel)	7	'	39	G	71	g	103
(bs)	8	(	40	H	72	h	104
(ht)	9	)	41	I	73	i	105
(nl)	10	*	42	J	74	j	106
(vt)	11	+	43	K	75	k	107
(np)	12	,	44	L	76	l	108
(cr)	13	-	45	M	77	m	109
(so)	14	.	46	N	78	n	110
(si)	15	/	47	O	79	o	111
(dle)	16	0	48	P	80	p	112
(dc1)	17	1	49	Q	81	q	113
(dc2)	18	2	50	R	82	r	114
(dc3)	19	3	51	S	83	s	115
(dc4)	20	4	52	T	84	t	116
(nak)	21	5	53	U	85	u	117
(syn)	22	6	54	V	86	v	118
(etb)	23	7	55	W	87	w	119
(can)	24	8	56	X	88	x	120
(em)	25	9	57	Y	89	y	121
(sub)	26	:	58	Z	90	z	122
(esc)	27	;	59	[	91	{	123
(fs)	28	<	60	\	92	|	124
(gs)	29	=	61	]	93	}	125
(rs)	30	>	62	^	94	~	126
(us)	31	?	63	_	95	(del)	127

This page lists C operators in order of *precedence* (highest to lowest). Their *associativity* indicates in what order operators of equal precedence in an expression are applied.

Operator	Description	Associativity
() [ ] ++ --	Parentheses (function call) Brackets (array subscript) Postfix increment/decrement	left-to-right
++ -- + - ! (*type*) * & sizeof	Prefix increment/decrement Unary plus/minus Logical negation Cast (change *type*) Dereference Address Determine size in bytes	right-to-left
* / %	Multiplication/division/modulus	left-to-right
+ -	Addition/subtraction	left-to-right
< <= > >=	Relational less than/less than or equal to Relational greater than/greater than or equal to	left-to-right
== !=	Relational is equal to/is not equal to	left-to-right
&&	Logical AND	left-to-right
||	Logical OR	left-to-right
?:	Ternary conditional	right-to-left
= += -= *= /= %=	Assignment Addition/subtraction assignment Multiplication/division assignment Modulus assignment	right-to-left
,	Comma (separate expressions)	left-to-right

CS 159 Midterm Exam #2
Tuesday November 7, 2017 [8:00pm – 9:30pm] – Loeb Playhouse
Instructor: William Crum
35 Questions * 3 Points Each = 105 Points
Any points earned beyond 100 are considered extra credit.

Exam Rules/Notices:

1. Complete your name and your student ID number on the answer sheet (write in AND bubble-in all requested information). There is no exam form or section to indicate on your answer sheet.
   - **An incorrect student ID number will result in a zero for this exam.** All student ID numbers begin with two zero digits. This must be written and "bubbled in" on your exam answer sheet.
   - **You must be in your assigned seat to receive credit for this exam.**

2. Make sure you have all 35 questions to this exam. You should answer every question. All questions only have one best answer. Please be careful when filling in your answers, any answer determined to be unreadable by Instructional Data Processing will be considered incorrect. Only the answer on your answer sheet can be considered when grading.
   - An **ASCII table** and **operator precedence table** have been provided on the back of this exam.

3. **NO QUESTIONS WILL BE ANSWERED DURING THE EXAM.** We do not answer questions during the exam due to the limited number of staff members present. It is easier for us to compensate for an erroneous test question than it is to answer questions or to effectively make an announcement during the examination period.
   - **Manage your time accordingly!**

4. You must assume that all C programs and code segments are implemented on the `guru.itap` machine and would be compiled with the `gcc` compiler as set up during the first week of the semester. When segments of code are presented you may assume that the appropriate include statements are present and that the code would be inside of a fully operational function or program.

5. **Protect your work and keep your focus on your own exam.** It is considered dishonest if you copy from another student or to permit another student to copy from you. Anyone found to violate course policies will receive a **failing grade for the course** and will be referred to the Office of the Dean of Students.

6. **You are NOT permitted to use any resources during this exam.** This includes but is not limited to; **texts, notes, calculators, cell phones, audio devices, and computers**. If your cell phone audibly rings during the exam you will be required to immediately submit your exam and leave the testing facility.

7. When you are finished with the exam, please proceed to the lobby to submit your answer form and to exit the facility. **You will be required to show photo identification before we can accept your work.** You will keep this exam form. You may not return to your seat once you have submitted your exam.

8. Scores and official exam answers will appear on Blackboard no later than Friday (Novmeber 10). Do not contact course staff members about mistakes (if any) until answers are posted. If you feel an error remains after answers have been posted you may make a written request for a regrade by Thursday November 16 and deliver it to HAAS G-26 (you may slide it under the door outside of office hours). Your request must be a hard copy (no e-mail) and include a detailed description, using code if applicable, demonstrating your belief why the posted answer is incorrect.

9. **When time is called ALL writing must stop.** You are not permitted to continue to make revisions to any answer on your exam once time has been called.

10. Schedule reminders:
    - **Lecture will meet on Thursday November 9.** Lecture on Tuesday November 21 has been canceled as compensation for this evening exam. **All lab sections meet this week.**

NO QUESTIONS WILL BE ANSWERED DURING THE EXAM.

Use the code segment below for problems 1 – 2

```
int x = 11;
int y = 5;
int z = 8;

int result;

result = x-- > 10 && y-- >= 5 || (++z % 2);

printf("x: %d y: %d\n", x, y);
printf("z + result: %d\n", z + result);
```

1. Which of the following is the output generated by the first print statement in the code segment above?
   A) x: 9 y: 4
   B) x: 10 y: 5
   C) x: 10 y: 4
   D) None of the above.

2. Which of the following is the output generated by the second print statement in the code segment above?
   A) z + result: 10
   B) z + result: 9
   C) z + result: 8
   D) None of the above.

3. Which of the following statements regarding the rules of the `switch` construct is FALSE?
   A) The expression that follows the keyword `case` may include a mathematical operator.
   B) The expression that follows the keyword `case` may include one or more constant operands.
   C) The expression that follows the keyword `case` must not represent the same value as any other `case`.
   D) None of the above.

4. Which of the following would be indicative of selecting the wrong looping construct for an iterative solution?
   A) Code found inside the body of the loop is also found again outside the body of the loop.
   B) The initialization of the loop control variable occurs inside the body of the loop.
   C) The update to the loop control variable is not the final action inside the body of the loop.
   D) None of the above.

5. Which of the following data types cannot be used to represent logical data?
   A) `long long`
   B) `double`
   C) `char`
   D) None of the above.

6. Which of the following statements regarding the course standards and the use of control-forcing statements is TRUE?
   A) Each user-defined function must be limited to at most a single `return` statement.
   B) The use of `break` must be limited to repetition constructs.
   C) The use of `continue` must be limited to selection constructs.
   D) None of the above.

```c
#include<stdio.h>

#define CUTOFF1 70
#define CUTOFF2 75
#define CUTOFF3 80

int main()
{
  int x = 75;
  int y = 68;
  int z = 81;
  int result = 0;

  if(y++ / CUTOFF3 || --x / CUTOFF3)
  {
    result = 1;
  }
  else if(x++ / CUTOFF2 || --z / CUTOFF3)
  {
    result += 2;
  }
  else if(--z / CUTOFF3 || ++y / CUTOFF1)
  {
    result += 3;
  }
  else
  {
    result += 4;
  }

  printf("x: %d y: %d\n", x, y);
  printf("z: %d result: %d\n", z, result);

  return(0);
}
```

7. Which of the following is the output generated by the first print statement in the program above?
   A) x: 74 y: 69
   B) x: 75 y: 69
   C) x: 76 y: 70
   D) None of the above.

8. Which of the following is the output generated by the second print statement in the program above?
   A) z: 80 result: 2
   B) z: 79 result: 3
   C) z: 81 result: 1
   D) None of the above.

9. Which of the following statements regarding input validation is FALSE?
   A) Input validation is one example of an event-controlled problem.
   B) Selection alone is not used to implement input validation because it provides only a finite number of opportunities for the user to input acceptable data.
   C) In this course you will be expected to validate that the input given is of the correct data type.
   D) None of the above.

```c
#include<stdio.h>

int condExpression(int);

int main()
{
  int result;

  result = condExpression(2000);
  result += condExpression(2016);
  result += condExpression(1900);
  result += condExpression(1800);

  printf("result: %d\n", result);

  return(0);
}

int condExpression(int y)
{
  return((!(y % 4) && (y % 100)) ? !(y % 400) : 0);
}
```

10. Which of the following is the output generated by the print statement in the program above?
    A) `result: 0`
    B) `result: 1`
    C) `result: 2`
    D) None of the above.

Use the code segment below for problems 11 – 12

```c
int i;
int ct = 0;

for(i = 1029; i >= 5; i /= 2)
{
  ct++;
}

printf("ct: %d\n", ct);
printf("i: %d\n", i);
```

11. Which of the following is the output generated by the first print statement in the code segment above?
    A) `ct: 8`
    B) `ct: 9`
    C) `ct: 10`
    D) None of the above.

12. Which of the following is the output generated by the second print statement in the code segment above?
    A) `i: 1`
    B) `i: 2`
    C) `i: 4`
    D) None of the above.

```c
#include<stdio.h>

int calcDays(int);

int main()
{
  int days;

  days = calcDays(5);
  days += calcDays(7);
  days += calcDays(2);

  printf("Result #1: %d\n", days);

  days = calcDays(10);
  days += calcDays(4);
  days += calcDays(0);

  printf("Result #2: %d\n", days);

  return(0);
}

int calcDays(int month)
{
  int days = 28;

  if(month > 6)
  {
    switch(month % 2)
    {
      case 0: days = 31;
      case 1: days = 30;
    }
  }
  else if(month != 2)
  {
    switch(month % 2)
    {
      case 1: days = 30;
      case 0: days = 31;
    }
  }

  return(days);
}
```

13. Which of the following is the output generated by the first print statement in the program above?
    A) Result #1: 88
    B) Result #1: 89
    C) Result #1: 90
    D) None of the above.

14. Which of the following is the output generated by the second print statement in the program above?
    A) Result #2: 89
    B) Result #2: 93
    C) Result #2: 92
    D) None of the above.

```c
#include<stdio.h>

int ctDigits(int);

int main()
{
  printf("Result #1: %d\n", ctDigits(1102003));

  printf("Result #2: %d\n", ctDigits(1222344));

  return(0);
}

int ctDigits(int n)
{
  int ct = 0;

  while(n >= 10)
  {
    if(n % 10 == n / 10 % 10)
    {
      ct++;
    }

    n = n / 10;
  }

  return(ct);
}
```

15. Which of the following is the output generated by the first print statement in the program above?
    A) `Result #1: 2`
    B) `Result #1: 3`
    C) `Result #1: 4`
    D) None of the above.

16. Which of the following is the output generated by the second print statement in the program above?
    A) `Result #2: 2`
    B) `Result #2: 3`
    C) `Result #2: 4`
    D) None of the above.

17. Which of the following statements regarding `for` loops is TRUE?
    A) According to the course standards a `for` loop should only be used with counter-controlled processes.
    B) According to the course standards if all three expressions are not needed in a `for` loop then you should include a token expression rather than omit one of the three `for` loop expressions.
    C) All `while` loops must be converted into `for` loops for counter-controlled processes.
    D) None of the above.

Use the program below for problems 18 – 19

```c
#include<stdio.h>

int ctDigits(int);

int main()
{
  printf("Result #1: %d\n", ctDigits(1234566));

  printf("Result #2: %d\n", ctDigits(12223333));

  return(0);
}

int ctDigits(int n)
{
  int ct = 0;
  int prevDigit;

  do
  {
    ct++;

    prevDigit = n % 10;
    n /= 10;
  }while(prevDigit == n % 10);

  return(ct);
}
```

18. Which of the following is the output generated by the first print statement in the program above?
    A) `Result #1: 2`
    B) `Result #1: 3`
    C) `Result #1: 4`
    D) None of the above.

19. Which of the following is the output generated by the second print statement in the program above?
    A) `Result #2: 2`
    B) `Result #2: 3`
    C) `Result #2: 5`
    D) None of the above.

20. Which of the following may result in the dangling else logical error?
    A) Using the assignment operator (=) when the equality operator (==) is expected.
    B) Failing to make proper use of { and } with a nested `if-else` construct.
    C) Testing two floating-point values for equality where small rounding errors result in a false evaluation.
    D) None of the above.

21. Which of the following statements regarding logical expressions is FALSE?
    A) The order of operations in a logical expression and its complement will be the same.
    B) The number of parentheses in a logical expression will be the same found in its complement.
    C) A logical expression that contains a NOT operator may also have a NOT operator in its complement.
    D) None of the above.

```c
#include<stdio.h>
#include<math.h>

int convertNumber(int, int);

int main()
{
  printf("Result #1: %d\n", convertNumber(1010, 0));

  printf("Result #2: %d\n", convertNumber(110, 4));

  return(0);
}

int convertNumber(int x, int y)
{
  int total = 0;

  if(x > 0)
  {
    total += convertNumber(x / 10, y + 1);
    total += x % 10 * pow(2, y);
  }

  return(total);
}
```

22. Which of the following is the output generated by the first print statement in the program above?
    A) `Result #1: 10`
    B) `Result #1: 20`
    C) `Result #1: 5`
    D) None of the above.

23. Which of the following is the output generated by the second print statement in the program above?
    A) `Result #2: 6`
    B) `Result #2: 48`
    C) `Result #2: 96`
    D) None of the above.

24. Which of the following statements regarding looping constructs if FALSE?
    A) In a `do-while` loop the number of times the loop control expression is evaluated is equal to the number of iterations.
    B) In a `for` loop the number of times the loop control expression is evaluated is one more than the number of iterations.
    C) In a `while` loop the number of times the loop control expression is evaluated is one more than the number of iterations.
    D) None of the above.

```
int i;
int j;
int k;
int ct = 0;

for(i = 1; i <= 10; i += 2)
{
  for(j = 1; j < i * 5; j++)
  {
    for(k = 1; k < i + j; k++)
    {
      ct++;
    }
  }
}

printf("i: %d j: %d\n", i, j);
printf("k: %d ct: %d\n", k, ct > 5000);
```

25. Which of the following is the output generated by the first print statement in the code segment above?
   A) i: 11 j: 50   C) i: 11 j: 45
   B) i: 10 j: 45   D) None of the above.

26. Which of the following is the output generated by the second print statement in the code segment above?
   A) k: 56 ct: 0   C) k: 53 ct: 1
   B) k: 55 ct: 0   D) None of the above.

Use the program below for problems 27 – 28

```
#include<stdio.h>

char convertNumber(int i);

int main()
{
  int x;

  printf("Result: %c\n", convertNumber(x));

  return(0);
}

char convertNumber(int i)
{
  return(i > 9 ? 'A' + (i - 10) : i > 5 ? 'z' - i : '0' + i);
}
```

27. Which of the following initial values of the integer variable x will generate Result: C as output?
   A) 3   C) 29
   B) 12   D) None of the above.

28. Which of the following initial values of the integer variable x will generate Result: r as output?
   A) 8   C) 27
   B) 17   D) None of the above.

Use the program below for problems 29 – 30

```c
#include<stdio.h>
#include<math.h>

int main()
{
  int i = 2;
  int j = 1;

  int num = 4;

  while(i++ % 3 != 0 || ++j % 3 != 0)
  {
    while(sqrt(num) - (int)sqrt(num) > 0)
    {
      num++;
    }
    num++;
  }

  printf("i: %d j: %d\n", i, j);

  printf("num: %d\n", num);

  return(0);
}
```

29. Which of the following is the output generated by the first print statement in the code segment above?
    A) i: 6 j: 3
    B) i: 7 j: 3
    C) i: 7 j: 4
    D) None of the above.

30. Which of the following is the output generated by the second print statement in the code segment above?
    A) num: 26
    B) num: 17
    C) num: 37
    D) None of the above.

31. Which of the following statements regarding nested selection and repetition is TRUE?
    A) In order for iterative processes to be considered nested they must appear in the same user-defined function.
    B) Iterative processes are only considered to be nested when both the inner and outer loop use the same type of looping construct.
    C) Nested selection often involves the evaluation of two different variables in the control expressions.
    D) None of the above.

32. Which of the following statements regarding the switch construct is FALSE?
    A) The default case is optional but when it is used it will not be followed by a constant expression.
    B) Because the control expression of a switch will generate a single value each constant expression that follows the keyword case must represent a single value.
    C) The executable statements represented by a case may include another switch construct.
    D) None of the above.

46

33. Which of the following statements regardng counter-controlled processes is FALSE?
    A) The loop control variable in a counter-controlled process can only be incremented or decremented by one.
    B) The total number of iterations in a counter-controlled process can be determined prior to the first iteration.
    C) An iterative solution to a counter-controlled process may include either pretest or post-test constructs.
    D) None of the above.

34. Which of the following statements is TRUE regarding redirection of output?
    A) Attempting to redirect output to an existing file will result in an error.
    B) The redirection of output is always accompanied by the use of redirection for input.
    C) When redirecting output it is all generated output that is sent to the external file.
    D) None of the above.

	Final Exam Grade			
	A	B	C	D and F
Last 4 Weeks	92.43%	88.79%	85.52%	63.91%
All Term	94.03%	90.84%	88.67%	74.43%

Class Average				
Last 4 Weeks	80.03%			
All Term	85.20%			

35. Each semester the attendance in lecture declines over the last four weeks of the term. This material represents the most difficult in the course and is the emphasis of the final exam. The data above demonstrates that those students with the largest change in attendance habits score the lowest on the final exam.
    A) Set a goal to finish with a strong level of participation in the course.
    B) Not the correct answer.
    C) Not the correct answer.
    D) Not the correct answer.

ASCII Table

Char	Dec	Char	Dec	Char	Dec	Char	Dec
delimiter	0	space	32	@	64	`	96
(soh)	1	!	33	A	65	a	97
(stx)	2	"	34	B	66	b	98
(etx)	3	#	35	C	67	c	99
(eot)	4	$	36	D	68	d	100
(enq)	5	%	37	E	69	e	101
(ack)	6	&	38	F	70	f	102
(bel)	7	'	39	G	71	g	103
(bs)	8	(	40	H	72	h	104
(ht)	9	)	41	I	73	i	105
(nl)	10	*	42	J	74	j	106
(vt)	11	+	43	K	75	k	107
(np)	12	,	44	L	76	l	108
(cr)	13	-	45	M	77	m	109
(so)	14	.	46	N	78	n	110
(si)	15	/	47	O	79	o	111
(dle)	16	0	48	P	80	p	112
(dc1)	17	1	49	Q	81	q	113
(dc2)	18	2	50	R	82	r	114
(dc3)	19	3	51	S	83	s	115
(dc4)	20	4	52	T	84	t	116
(nak)	21	5	53	U	85	u	117
(syn)	22	6	54	V	86	v	118
(etb)	23	7	55	W	87	w	119
(can)	24	8	56	X	88	x	120
(em)	25	9	57	Y	89	y	121
(sub)	26	:	58	Z	90	z	122
(esc)	27	;	59	[	91	{	123
(fs)	28	<	60	\	92	|	124
(gs)	29	=	61	]	93	}	125
(rs)	30	>	62	^	94	~	126
(us)	31	?	63	_	95	(del)	127

This page lists C operators in order of *precedence* (highest to lowest). Their *associativity* indicates in what order operators of equal precedence in an expression are applied.

Operator	Description	Associativity

`()`
`[]`
`++ --`
	Parentheses (function call)
	Brackets (array subscript)
	Postfix increment/decrement
		left-to-right

`++ --`
`+ -`
`!`
`(type)`
`*`
`&`
`sizeof`
	Prefix increment/decrement
	Unary plus/minus
	Logical negation
	Cast (change *type*)
	Dereference
	Address
	Determine size in bytes
		right-to-left

`* / %`	Multiplication/division/modulus	left-to-right
`+ -`	Addition/subtraction	left-to-right
`< <=` `> >=`	Relational less than/less than or equal to Relational greater than/greater than or equal to	left-to-right
`== !=`	Relational is equal to/is not equal to	left-to-right
`&&`	Logical AND	left-to-right
`||`	Logical OR	left-to-right
`?:`	Ternary conditional	right-to-left

`=`
`+= -=`
`*= /=`
`%=`
	Assignment
	Addition/subtraction assignment
	Multiplication/division assignment
	Modulus assignment
		right-to-left

`,`	Comma (separate expressions)	left-to-right

CS 159 Final Exam

Thursday May 4, 2017
8:00am – 10:00am – Elliott Hall of Music
50 Questions * 3 Points Each = 150 Points

Exam Rules/Notices:

1. Complete your name and your student ID number on the answer sheet (write in AND bubble-in all requested information). **An incorrect student ID number will result in a zero for this exam.** All student ID numbers begin with two zero digits. **You must be in your assigned seat to receive credit for this exam.** There is no exam form to indicate on your answer sheet.

2. **Make sure you have all 50 questions to this exam.** You should answer every question. All questions only have one best answer. Please be careful when filling in your answers, any answer determined to be unreadable by Instructional Data Processing will be considered incorrect. Only the answer on your answer sheet can be considered when grading.
   - An **operator precedence and ASCII table** have been provided on the back of this exam.

3. **NO QUESTIONS WILL BE ANSWERED DURING THE EXAM.** We do not answer questions during the exam due to the limited number of staff members present. It is easier for us to compensate for an erroneous test question than it is to answer questions or to effectively make an announcement during the examination period.
   - **Manage your time accordingly!**

4. You must assume that all C programs and code segments are implemented on the `guru.itap` machine and would be compiled with the `gcc` compiler as set up during the first week of the semester. When segments of code are presented you may assume that the appropriate include statements are present and that the code would be inside of a fully operational function or program. Only question **#49** is related to **MATLAB/Octave**.

5. **Protect your work and keep your focus on your own exam.** It is considered dishonest if you copy from another student or to permit another student to copy from you. Anyone found to violate course policies will receive a **failing grade for the course** and will be referred to the Office of the Dean of Students.

6. **You are NOT permitted to use any resources during this exam.** This includes but is not limited to; **texts, notes, calculators, cell phones, audio devices, and computers**. If your cell phone audibly rings during the exam you will be required to immediately submit your exam and leave the testing facility.

7. When you are finished with the exam, please proceed to the lobby to submit your answer form and to exit the facility. **You will be required to show photo identification before we can accept your work.** You will keep this exam paper. You may not return to your seat once you have submitted your exam.

8. **When time is called or when leaving your seat to submit your exam ALL writing must stop.** At either of these times you are no longer permitted to make revisions on your exam.

9. **Scores and official exam answers will appear on Blackboard no later than Monday (May 8).** Do not contact course staff members about mistakes (if any) until answers are posted. If you feel an error remains after answers have been posted you may make an e-mail request (wcrum AT purdue DOT edu) **from your Purdue e-mail** account for a regrade within five days of the answers and scores being released. Your request must include a description (using code if applicable) demonstrating why the posted answer is incorrect.

10. **Final course grades** and the announcement of the minimums points required for each letter grade will be posted on the afternoon of Tuesday May 9. **Grades are ONLY assigned based on points earned.**
    Note the following before you contact course staff members regarding your course grade:
    - **Wait** until minimums for each letter grade are announced, be sure to use only your **Purdue e-mail address,** and **provide specific concerns** you have with specific assignments as grades in the course will be based on **points earned** and not factors external to the course.
    - Regrade requests or Blackboard Learn errors on older assignments must be addressed before leaving campus by printing up your concern and sliding it under William Crum's office door (HAAS G-26).
    - Please allow sufficient time for your circumstance to be considered and a detailed reply given.

11. **About Question #50.** If your lecture section met twice a week then you will select answer A for the final problem. If your lecture section only met once a week on Thursday afternoons at 4:30pm then your answer for the final problem is B. Selecting the wrong answer for the final problem or failing to comply with all of the above instructions may result in no credit for this exam.

NO QUESTIONS WILL BE ANSWERED DURING THE EXAM.

Use the program below for problems 1 – 2

```c
#include<stdio.h>

#define SIZE 9

int main()
{
  int x[SIZE] = {0, 5, 4, 1, 2, 7, 8, 6};
  int i;

  for(i = 1; i < SIZE - 1; i++)
  {
    x[i - 1] = x[i] * x[i + 1];
  }

  printf("x[3] = %d\n", x[3]);
  printf("x[8] = %d\n", x[8]);

  return(0);
}
```

1. Which of the following is the first line of output generated in the program on the left?
   A) x[3] = 0
   B) x[3] = 8
   C) x[3] = 14
   D) None of the above.

2. Which of the following is the second line of output generated in the program on the left?
   A) x[8] = 0
   B) x[8] = 6
   C) x[8] = 8
   D) None of the above.

```
#include<stdio.h>

#define SIZE 11

int main()
{
  int x[SIZE] = {1, 1, 1, 1, 1, 1, 1, 1, 1, 1};

  int i;
  int j;

  for(i = 2; i <= SIZE / 2; i++)
  {
    for(j = 2; j <= SIZE / i; j++)
    {
      x[i * j] = 0;
    }
  }

  printf("x[2] = %d\n", x[2]);
  printf("x[5] = %d\n", x[5]);
  printf("x[9] = %d\n", x[9]);

  return(0);
}
```

3. Which of the following is the first line of output generated in the program on the left?
   A) x[2] = 0
   B) x[2] = 1
   C) x[2] = 2
   D) None of the above.

4. Which of the following is the second line of output generated in the program on the left?
   A) x[5] = 0
   B) x[5] = 1
   C) x[5] = 5
   D) None of the above.

5. Which of the following is the third line of output generated in the program above?
   A) x[9] = 0
   B) x[9] = 1
   C) x[9] = 3
   D) None of the above.

Use the program below for problems 6 – 8

```c
#include<stdio.h>

#define SIZE 10

void initArray(int[]);
int changeArray(int[], int, int);

int main()
{
  int x[SIZE];
  int index;

  initArray(x);
  index = changeArray(x, 0, 6);
  index = changeArray(x, index, 6);
  index = changeArray(x, index, 6);

  printf("index: %d\n", index);
  printf("x[1]: %d\n", x[1]);
  printf("x[6]: %d\n", x[6]);

  return(0);
}

void initArray(int x[])
{
  int i;

  for(i = 1; i <= SIZE; i++)
  {
    x[i - 1] = i;
  }
}

int changeArray(int y[], int i, int ct)
{
  while(ct > 0)
  {
    if(y[i % SIZE] != 0)
    {
      ct--;
    }

    i++;
  }

  y[(i - 1) % SIZE] = 0;

  return(i);
}
```

6. Which of the following is the first line of output generated in the program on the left?
   A) `index: 0`
   B) `index: 9`
   C) `index: 19`
   D) None of the above.

7. Which of the following is the second line of output generated in the program on the left?
   A) `x[1]: 0`
   B) `x[1]: 1`
   C) `x[1]: 2`
   D) None of the above.

8. Which of the following is the third line of output generated in the program on the left?
   A) `x[6]: 0`
   B) `x[6]: 1`
   C) `x[6]: 7`
   D) None of the above.

54

```c
#include<stdio.h>

#define SIZE 8

void changeArray(int[], int);

int main()
{
  int x[SIZE] = {40, 60, 20, 30, 55, 45, 5, 25};
  int i;

  for(i = 0; i < SIZE / 2; i++)
  {
    changeArray(x, i % 2);
  }

  printf("x[3] = %d\n", x[3]);
  printf("x[5] = %d\n", x[5]);

  return(0);
}

void changeArray(int x[], int j)
{
  int temp;
  int i;

  for(i = j; i < SIZE - 1; i += 2)
  {
    if(x[i] > x[i + 1])
    {
      temp = x[i];
      x[i] = x[i + 1];
      x[i + 1] = temp;
    }
  }
}
```

9. Which of the following is the first line of output generated in the program above?
   A) x[3] = 5
   B) x[3] = 25
   C) x[3] = 60
   D) None of the above.

10. Which of the following is the second line of output generated in the program above?
    A) x[5] = 25
    B) x[5] = 45
    C) x[5] = 55
    D) None of the above.

```
1 #include<stdio.h>
2 #define SIZE 10
3
4 void sorts(int[], int[]);
5
6 int main()
7 {
8    int data[SIZE] = {5, 11, 9, 8, 10, 1, 13, 7, 6, 2};
9    int status[SIZE] = {1, 1, 1, 0, 0, 1, 1, 1, 0, 0};
10
11   sorts(data, status);
12   sorts(status, data);
13
14   printf("index 3 = %d %d\n", data[3], status[3]);
15   printf("index 6 = %d %d\n", data[6], status[6]);
16
17   return(0);
18 }
19
20 void sorts(int x[], int y[])
21 {
22   int numPasses;
23   int lcv;
24   int temp;
25
26   for(numPasses = 1; numPasses < SIZE; numPasses++)
27   {
28     for(lcv = 0; lcv < SIZE - numPasses; lcv++)
29     {
30       if(x[lcv] > x[lcv + 1])
31       {
32         temp = x[lcv];
33         x[lcv] = x[lcv + 1];
34         x[lcv + 1] = temp;
35
36         temp = y[lcv];
37         y[lcv] = y[lcv + 1];
38         y[lcv + 1] = temp;
39       }
40     }
41   }
42 }
```

11. Which of the following is the first line of output generated in the program above?
    A) `index 3 = 6 0`   C) `index 3 = 10 0`
    B) `index 3 = 8 0`   D) None of the above.

12. Which of the following is the second line of output generated in the program above?
    A) `index 6 = 9 1`   C) `index 6 = 5 1`
    B) `index 6 = 7 1`   D) None of the above.

13. Which of the following changes to the sorting function above will reverse the order in which the data is ultimately sorted?
    A) Replace > with < on line 30.   C) Revise the `for` loop on line 28 to count down
    B) Replace `x[lcv + 1]` with `x[lcv - 1]` on   from `SIZE - numPasses - 1` to zero.
       line 30.   D) None of the above.

56

14. Given the 14-element array below:

        8   8   11   11   15   15   18   18   20   20   21   21   23   23

Which of the following are the final values of the first and last variables when applying the binary search algorithm to locate a target value of 22?

A) first = 11 last = 11
B) first = 12 last = 11
C) first = 10 last = 11
D) None of the above.

15. Given the 14-element array below:

        8   8   11   11   15   15   18   18   20   20   21   21   23   23

Which of the following are the final values of the first and last variables when applying the binary search algorithm to locate a target value of 9?

A) first = 1 last = 1
B) first = 2 last = 1
C) first = 1 last = 0
D) None of the above.

16. Given the following 8-element array:

    7   14   21   35   42   28   14   7

and the array after two passes:

    42   35   7   14   21   28   14   7

Which of the following sorting algorithms have been applied?

A) Selection
B) Bubble
C) Insertion
D) More than one of the above.

17. Given the following 8-element array:

    7   14   21   35   42   28   14   7

and the array after two passes:

    7   14   21   35   42   28   14   7

Which of the following sorting algorithms have been applied?

A) Selection
B) Bubble
C) Insertion
D) More than one of the above.

```
#include<stdio.h>

#define SIZE 9

int main()
{
   int x[SIZE] = {0, 5, 4, 1, 2, 7, 8, 6};
   int i;

   printf("x = %d\n", x);

   return(0);
}
```

18. Which of the following describes the integer value that will be displayed by the print statement in the program above?
    A) The value displayed will be the first element of the array.
    B) The value displayed will be the declared size of the array.
    C) The value displayed will be the final element of the array.
    D) None of the above.

Use the program below for problems 19 – 20

```
#define XLENGTH 10
#define YLENGTH 5
#define ZLENGTH 15

int main()
{
   int x[XLENGTH][YLENGTH][ZLENGTH];

   getData(x);
   printArray(x);

   return(0);
}
```

19. Which of the following would be the correct declaration of the getData user-defined function as used in the code segment above?
    A) void getData(int[][][]);
    B) void getData(int[][][ZLENGTH]);
    C) void getData(int[][YLENGTH][ZLENGTH]);
    D) None of the above.

20. Which of the following statements regarding the multidimensional integer array x in the code segment above is TRUE?
    A) The last element of the array is x[XLENGTH - 1][YLENGTH - 1][ZLENGTH - 1].
    B) The first element of the array is x[0][1][1].
    C) The total capacity of the array is 775 integers.
    D) None of the above.

```
int x = 17;
int y = 11;

int *ptr1;
int *ptr2;

ptr1 = &x;
ptr2 = ptr1;

*ptr1 = 10;

ptr1 = &y;

*ptr2 = 13;

printf("x: %d\n", x);
printf("y: %d\n", y);
```

21. Which of the following is the first line of output generated in the code segment above?
   A) x: 10
   B) x: 13
   C) x: 17
   D) None of the above.

22. Which of the following is the second line of output generated in the code segment above?
   A) y: 11
   B) y: 10
   C) y: 13
   D) None of the above.

23. Which of the following statements regarding the sorting algorithms introduced this semester is TRUE?
   A) Once a value is placed in the sorted list it may move again during the remainder of the selection sorting process.
   B) The bubble sorting algorithm will compare all neighboring elements in the array on each and every pass.
   C) The logic of the insertion sorting algorithm may reach a state where there exists only one value in the unsorted list.
   D) None of the above.

24. Which of the following statements regarding arrays and functions is FALSE?
   A) It is not possible to pass the whole array to a function by value.
   B) It is possible to pass elements of an array to a function by address.
   C) If one parameter is passed by address to a user-defined function then all of the parameters to that function must be passed by address.
   D) None of the above.

25. Which of the following statements regarding the array searching algorithms introduced this semester is TRUE?
   A) The binary searching algorithm will always find a target value present in an array faster than the linear/sequential searching algorithm.
   B) When the data is not in a sorted state and a value in the data set is not unique then we must compare every element with the target to obtain an accurate count of the number of times it is present.
   C) The linear/sequential searching algorithm cannot be applied to an array in which the data is in a sorted state.
   D) None of the above.

```c
#include<stdio.h>
#include<string.h>

#define SIZE 20

int main()
{
  char str[SIZE] = "Go Purdue!";
  char str2[SIZE] = "Beat Indiana!";
  int length;

  strcpy(str2, str);

  length = strlen(str);

  str[length - 1] = 's';
  str[length] = '!';
  str[length + 1] = '\0';

  printf("length: %d\n", length);
  printf("str: %s\n", str);

  return(0);
}
```

26. Which of the following is the first line of output generated in the program above?
    A) `length: 12`   C) `length: 9`
    B) `length: 10`   D) None of the above.

27. Which of the following is the second line of output generated in the program above?
    A) `str: s!`   C) `str: Go Purdues!`
    B) `str: Beat Indianas!`   D) None of the above.

28. Which of the following describes what makes the `gets` function "dangerous and should not be used" according to the compiler?
    A) The input entered by the user will not be terminated with a delimiter character.
    B) There is a potential that the user may enter digit values which cannot be stored in a string.
    C) No limits are in place to ensure that the amount of data entered does not exceed the capacity of the array.
    D) None of the above.

29. Which of the following statements regarding arrays in the C programming language is FALSE?
    A) In a fixed-length array the size of the array is known when the program is compiled.
    B) The index value represents an offset from the beginning of the array to the element being referenced.
    C) When accessing an array element the C language does not check whether the index is within the boundary of an array.
    D) None of the above.

30. Which of the following statements regarding redirection is FALSE?
    A) Redirecting output (>) to an existing file will result in any existing data in that file being lost.
    B) Redirecting output (>>) to a file that does not exist will result in an error.
    C) The use of redirection with both input and output in the same statement is common but not required.
    D) None of the above.

61

```c
#include<stdio.h>
#include<math.h>

#define SIZE 35

int numCheck(int);

int main()
{
  int data[SIZE] = {0};
  int i;

  for(i = 0; i < SIZE; i++)
  {
    data[i] = numCheck(i);
  }

  printf("data[1] = %d\n", data[1]);
  printf("data[11] = %d\n", data[11]);
  printf("data[25] = %d\n", data[25]);

  return(0);
}

int numCheck(int num)
{
  int root;

  root = (int)sqrt(num);

  while(root > 0 && num % root)
  {
    root--;
  }

  return(!(root - 1));
}
```

31. Which of the following is the first line of output generated in the program above?
    A) data[1] = -1   C) data[1] = 1
    B) data[1] = 0   D) None of the above.

32. Which of the following is the second line of output generated in the program above?
    A) data[11] = -1   C) data[11] = 1
    B) data[11] = 0   D) None of the above.

33. Which of the following is the third line of output generated in the program above?
    A) data[25] = 4   C) data[25] = 1
    B) data[25] = 0   D) None of the above.

```c
#include<stdio.h>
#include<math.h>

#define VOLUME (4 / 3 * M_PI)
#define SURF_AREA 3 * VOLUME

int main()
{
  int radius = 2;
  double vol;
  double sArea;

  vol = (double) VOLUME * pow(radius, 3);

  sArea = pow(radius, 2) * SURF_AREA;

  printf("Volume: %.1lf\n", vol);
  printf("Surface Area: %.1lf\n", sArea);
  printf("Radius: %.*f\n", radius, (float) radius);

  return(0);
}
```

34. Which of the following is the first line of output generated in the program above?
    A) Volume: 18.8
    B) Volume: 33.5
    C) Volume: 25.1
    D) None of the above.

35. Which of the following is the second line of output generated in the program above?
    A) Surface Area: 50.3
    B) Surface Area: 37.7
    C) Surface Area: 18.8
    D) None of the above.

36. Which of the following is the third line of output generated in the program above?
    A) Radius: 2.000000
    B) Radius: 2.0
    C) Radius: 2.00
    D) None of the above.

37. Which of the following statements regarding compiler-generated notifications is TRUE?
    A) Modification of a single variable more than once in an expression is a compiler-generated error that will not result in a new executable file being created.
    B) The dangling else error where a nested `else` is automatically paired with the previous `if` is a compiler-generated error that will not result in a new executable file being created.
    C) The use of a variable before it is initialized is a compiler-generated error that will not result in a new executable file being created.
    D) None of the above.

```c
#include<stdio.h>

int testValue(int, int);
void printData(int, int, int);

int main()
{
  int n = 48293;
  int ct = 0;
  int call = 1;

  do
  {
    ct += testValue(n / 10, n % 10);
    printData(call++, n, ct);
    n /= 10;
  }while(n > 0);

  return(0);
}

void printData(int call, int num, int ct)
{
  printf("-=-=-=-=-=-=-=-\n");
  printf("%d Number: %*d\n", call, ct, num);
}

int testValue(int num, int digit)
{
  int ct = 0;

  while(num > 0)
  {
    ct += num % 10 <= digit ? 1 : 0;
    num /= 10;
  }

  return(ct);
}
```

38. Which of the following is the output generated by the first call to the `printData` function in the program above?

`-=-=-=-=-=-=-=-` `1 Number: 4` **A**	`-=-=-=-=-=-=-=-` `1 Number:      48293` **C**
`-=-=-=-=-=-=-=-` `1 Number: 48293` **B**	None of the Above. **D**

39. Which of the following is the output generated by the fourth call to the `printData` function in the program above?

`-=-=-=-=-=-=-=-` `4 Number:    48` **A**	`-=-=-=-=-=-=-=-` `4 Number:    48` **C**
`-=-=-=-=-=-=-=-` `4 Number:    48` **B**	None of the above. **D**

```
int x = 699871;

while(x > 10)
{
  switch(x % 100 >= 97)
  {
    case 1: printf("%c", x % 100 - 32);
            break;
    case 0: printf("%c", x % 100);
  }

  x /= 10;
}
```

40. Which of the following is the output generated by the code segment above?
    A) GWbcE
    B) gwbce
    C) GWBCE
    D) None of the above.

41. Which of the following is the output generated by the code segment above if they break statement were to be removed?
    A) GWBbCcE
    B) GWbcE
    C) GWBBCCE
    D) None of the above.

Use the program below for problems 42 – 43

```
int x = 11;
int y = 6;
int z = 17;

int result;

result = ++z % x && y++ % 2;
result += z % y && (x + 1) % y;
result += x % y > 1 && y % z++ > 1;
result += ++x >= y * 2 || y % 2 && z++ % 2;

printf("x: %d y: %d z: %d\n", x, y, z);
printf("result: %d\n", result);
```

42. Which of the following is the first line of output generated in the program above?
    A) x: 12 y: 6 z: 19   C) x: 12 y: 7 z: 20
    B) x: 13 y: 6 z: 19   D) None of the above.

43. Which of the following is the second line of output generated in the program above?
    A) result: 1   C) result: 3
    B) result: 2   D) None of the above.

44. Which of the following regarding the modification of the value of a variable is FALSE?
    A) An implicit type conversion may result in data truncation when applied to an assignment statement.
    B) An explicit type conversion has the ability to alter the data type of a variable for the current statement and the remainder of the program.
    C) A post-fix increment applied to a variable will make use of the current value within the expression and then variable will be updated for use in the next expression.
    D) None of the above.

45. Which of the following statements regarding the programming and documentation standards is TRUE?
    A) Each user-defined function is limited to at most one `return` statement.
    B) While most variables in a user-defined function should be declared in the local declaration section it is also acceptable to declare the occasional variable among the executable statements of the function.
    C) Simple input and output statements may be found inside of the `main` function.
    D) None of the above.

46. Which of the following statements regarding the formatting of output with the `printf` function is FALSE?
    A) The use of the flag option in a placeholder could shift the alignment of data from right-aligned to left-aligned when used with a sufficiently large width modifier.
    B) The precision modifier is limited to use only with those data types in the floating-point family.
    C) The size option of a placeholder may be used with those longer data types within the integer and floating-point families.
    D) None of the above.

47. Which of the following statements regarding the course standards and the proper use of `for` loops is TRUE?
    A) The `for` loop should be limited to event-controlled processes.
    B) A `for` loop should always make use of all three of its expressions.
    C) The `for` loop will eliminate the need for the `while` loop in pretest processes.
    D) All of the above.

Use the code segment below for problem 48

```
char grade;   //ASSUME VARIABLE INITIALIED BY USER INPUT
int pts;

switch(grade)
{
   case 'A' + 5: pts = 0;
                 break;
   case 'A':     pts = 1;
   case 'A' + 1: pts++;
   case 'A' + 2: pts++;
   case 'A' + 3: pts++;
}
```

48. Which of the following rules of a `switch` construct is being violated in the code segment above?
    A) Each case must be followed by a constant expression.
    B) The data type of the control expression is integral.
    C) No two cases can represent the same value.
    D) None of the above.

49. Which of the following statements regarding the file functions in **MATLAB/Octave** is TRUE?
    A) The `fopen` function will return a zero value when the external connection attempt fails.
    B) The parameter to the `fclose` function is the name of the external data file.
    C) The `feof` function will return a logically true value when the end of the file has been reached.
    D) None of the above.

50. The answer to this final problem can be found on the cover of the exam.
    A)
    B)
    C)
    D)

ASCII Table

Char	Dec	Char	Dec	Char	Dec	Char	Dec
delimiter	0	space	32	@	64	`	96
(soh)	1	!	33	A	65	a	97
(stx)	2	"	34	B	66	b	98
(etx)	3	#	35	C	67	c	99
(eot)	4	$	36	D	68	d	100
(enq)	5	%	37	E	69	e	101
(ack)	6	&	38	F	70	f	102
(bel)	7	'	39	G	71	g	103
(bs)	8	(	40	H	72	h	104
(ht)	9	)	41	I	73	i	105
(nl)	10	*	42	J	74	j	106
(vt)	11	+	43	K	75	k	107
(np)	12	,	44	L	76	l	108
(cr)	13	-	45	M	77	m	109
(so)	14	.	46	N	78	n	110
(si)	15	/	47	O	79	o	111
(dle)	16	0	48	P	80	p	112
(dc1)	17	1	49	Q	81	q	113
(dc2)	18	2	50	R	82	r	114
(dc3)	19	3	51	S	83	s	115
(dc4)	20	4	52	T	84	t	116
(nak)	21	5	53	U	85	u	117
(syn)	22	6	54	V	86	v	118
(etb)	23	7	55	W	87	w	119
(can)	24	8	56	X	88	x	120
(em)	25	9	57	Y	89	y	121
(sub)	26	:	58	Z	90	z	122
(esc)	27	;	59	[	91	{	123
(fs)	28	<	60	\	92	|	124
(gs)	29	=	61	]	93	}	125
(rs)	30	>	62	^	94	~	126
(us)	31	?	63	_	95	(del)	127

This page lists C operators in order of *precedence* (highest to lowest). Their *associativity* indicates in what order operators of equal precedence in an expression are applied.

Operator	Description	Associativity

`()`
 `[]`
 `++ --`
	Parentheses (function call)
	 Brackets (array subscript)
	 Postfix increment/decrement
		left-to-right

`++ --`
 `+ -`
 `!`
 `(type)`
 `*`
 `&`
 `sizeof`
	Prefix increment/decrement
	 Unary plus/minus
	 Logical negation
	 Cast (change *type*)
	 Dereference
	 Address
	 Determine size in bytes
		right-to-left

`* / %`	Multiplication/division/modulus	left-to-right
`+ -`	Addition/subtraction	left-to-right
`< <=` `> >=`	Relational less than/less than or equal to Relational greater than/greater than or equal to	left-to-right
`== !=`	Relational is equal to/is not equal to	left-to-right
`&&`	Logical AND	left-to-right
`||`	Logical OR	left-to-right
`?:`	Ternary conditional	right-to-left

`=`
 `+= -=`
 `*= /=`
 `%=`
	Assignment
	 Addition/subtraction assignment
	 Multiplication/division assignment
	 Modulus assignment
		right-to-left

`,`	Comma (separate expressions)	left-to-right

LECTURE NOTES

- ✓ Chapter 1 – Introduction to Computers
- ✓ Chapter 2 – Introduction to the C Language
- ✓ Chapter 3 – The Structure of a C Program
- ✓ Chapter 4 – User/Programmer-Defined Functions
- ✓ Introduction to Problem Solving Techniques
- ✓ Chapter 5 – Selection
- ✓ Chapter 6 – Repetition
- ✓ Chapter 7 – External File Input/Output
- ✓ Chapter 8 – Arrays
- ✓ Chapter 11 – Strings
- ✓ Chapters 9/10 – Pointers and Pointer Applications

Chapter 1 – Introduction to Computers

Hardware Basics

The four primary components of a computer:

1. A CPU (processor)
2. Main Memory (RAM)
3. I/O (Printers, Monitors, Disk Drives)
4. Systems Interconnection (a method of connecting all of the above)

The following two hardware components of a computer are important to us as programmers:

1. The processor or CPU.
2. The primary memory storage, RAM.

- **Why these two particular components?** An understanding of how the CPU works and what RAM accomplishes for our program will allow us to better utilize these limited resources of the computer.

71

Primary Memory (RAM)

- The memory of a computer will store the **instructions** and **data** of the programs that we will write this semester.

- You may have made the observation that the capacity of RAM (4-8 GB) on your personal machine is quite small in comparison to the size of your hard drive (500-1000 or more GB). Therefore, not every instruction or data associated with the currently executing program can be stored in primary memory, but, when instructions or data are needed, they must be **fetched, or retrieved,** from the hard drive and brought in to primary memory for use.

- Similar to addresses of homes on a street, the memory of the computer has addresses at which instructions and data can be stored.

- In our programs we will rename these addresses with names that are more meaningful to us as programmers rather than referencing a specific address in memory to locate the desired data.

The **CPU** is of interest as it is where all of the processing of **instructions and associated data** will take place. The CPU can be described as having four fundamental components:

1. Registers - A small amount of memory local to the CPU used for temporary storage related to the current instruction being processed.
2. ALU - Hardware responsible for the calculations required of an instruction.
3. Control Unit - Coordinates the operations of the CPU.
4. Internal CPU Interconnection - A mechanism connecting all of the above.

The CPU

- The Central Processing Unit coordinates and performs the operations of the computer.
- The CPU executes instructions (of an operation) through a process known as the **instruction cycle**.

Instruction Cycle Diagram:

Steps of the Instruction Cycle:

Memory Hierarchy:

Why is secondary memory slower than primary memory?

If primary memory is faster then why not grow the capacity of this level and eliminate secondary memory?

73

Natural Languages versus Machine Languages

- When we describe problems that we wish to solve we do so in a **natural language**.
- **Natural languages** are spoken and have evolved over centuries in accordance with their usage.
- **Natural languages** are full of attributes that are unfit for use by a computer.

The Idea of a Programming Language

To give instructions to a computer this semester, we will use a **programming language**, in particular, the C programming language. The C programming language is composed of keywords that come from a natural language but are used without the ambiguity. Initially the C programming language syntax will look foreign to you as a beginner, but it is completely unreadable by the computer!

The computer has its own language, called a **machine language** that it can interpret as instructions specific to the individual machine will perform the task. This machine language is written only in 0's and 1's because the internal circuits of a computer are made of switches, transistors, and other electronic devices can be in one of two states: off (0) or on (1).

It didn't take long for programmers to realize that coding in a machine language is very challenging and the entire process of developing, debugging, and maintaining instructions in a machine language is not something most would enjoy doing. A process of evolution away from a machine language towards a natural language has been ongoing and has resulted in the programming languages of today.

Natural Languages

Machine Languages

Other concerns with low-level languages:

- Instructions written specifically for the hardware of one machine cannot be used easily on a different machine.
- Requires the programmer to consider the algorithm in small, incremental steps.
- Programmer left with the task of managing memory.

How does the computer of today understand these high level programming languages if all a computer instructions are composed of 0's and 1's (binary numbers)?

74

Creating and Running Programs

To answer the previous question we must explore the process of turning a C program into a file that can be executed on the local machine.

The programming process is composed of steps which are repeated many times during development:

Writing and Editing the Program

The first step is **writing** the program (actually, the first step is developing your solution, but we are describing the implementation of the solution at this time) which will require the use of a piece of software known as a **text editor**. The text editor of choice for this semester will be **vi** (pronounced vee-eye). If you know of another UNIX based editor, you are welcome to use it but as with all editors you assume responsibility for understanding its operation. We find the use of vi to be a powerful one for writing code. Please understand that there is a learning curve to vi, but with enough **practice** you too will be working with vi comfortably!

Saving the Changes

Please keep in mind the importance of **saving your work regularly!** Too many students in the past have lost a significant amount of unsaved work by a dropped connection, frozen computer, or power outage because they failed to save their work as they progressed.

- **You should test your work regularly too!** It is easy to write a lot of code and then only to find numerous errors or such a bad design that correcting all of the problems would be more difficult than starting over!
- **Testing regularly** should not imply you should create your solution while coding, but it cannot be stressed enough that when you write code it should be nothing more than the implementation of a well designed algorithm. Without planning your solution is being developed through trial and error which tends to be an inefficient and frustrating process.
- **It is possible to make multiple-submissions for a given assignment.** However, it is only the last submission that is kept for grading. ALL previous submissions by the same individual are over-written and cannot be restored.

In your collaborative lab groups, and for each lab assignment, you must designate a single individual who will make all submissions for the group. **Group members cannot overwrite submissions made by the other members.** This will lead to confusion when it comes time for your lab instructor to determine which submission to grade.

75

Example: Assume we are implementing the solution to a problem and have progressed in our coding to the point that we need to test what we have input so far.

What should be done next?

1. Save the work to make sure the **source file** of our C code has been stored and reflects our most recent changes.
2. Send the source file to the **compiler** so that the source file can be prepared to be executed by the computer.

The Compiler

The compiler is in a category of software that is used to convert the source programming language code into the machine language of the computer.

The compiling process has **two phases of interest to us:**

1. The **preprocessor** - reads the source code and prepares it for the translator. There are special instructions known as **preprocessor directives** that you can give the preprocessor to prepare the source code for translation.
2. The **translator** - does the actual work of converting your program into machine language.

The linker at the end of the process above assembles all of the functions of your program (some of which may come from the system library) into the executable program.

- The linker is actually another piece of software separate from the compiler.
- On our systems all of the steps in the process are completed with a single instruction which may be transparent to the programmer.

Figure 1-10 found on page 11 of your C programming text:

Program Execution (Testing/Running the Executable File)

Upon successful compilation (we will talk about unsuccessful compilation later) an executable file will be created. By default the name of this executable file is `a.out`. To execute, or run, the program you need only type `a.out` at the UNIX prompt. It is assumed that you are in the same directory as the `a.out` file while doing most of your testing.

Each time you modify the source file you must recompile the code and create a new `a.out` to see the changes as reflected in your source code. A new executable file will replace any previously existing one. In most cases keeping the old executable file is not desired.

- If compilation of your program fails no new executable file will be created.
- A failed compilation attempt may not result an existing `a.out` file being removed/deleted.

Program Development

Our goal in CS 159: to be able to develop solutions to problems without considering any specific syntax of the programming language that you may potentially use.

Exposure to good programming practices is important to introduce the methods necessary to designing "a program that produces correct results, is well-designed, is efficient, and adheres to documentation and programming standards of the course."

Structure Charts

- Large programs are complex structures consisting of many interrelated parts and must be carefully designed.
- The structure chart shows how we are going to break out problem into logical sub problems and how data will flow in between these modules.
- More in Chapter 4.

77

Flowcharts

- The purpose of a flowchart is to describe visually the logic of a function.
- A flowchart should be developed for each sub problem identified on a structure chart.

Each step in planning will assist you in eliminating logical errors that are often very time consuming to resolve.

Problem: Given a loan amount, annual interest rate, and the term of the loan in years, determine the monthly payment.

Step #1 – What is specified of the program?

- Input – Three values. Loan amount, annual interest rate, and term.
- Output – Monthly payment.

Step #2 – Analyze the problem

- What type of mathematical operations do we need?

Variable	Description	Expression
years	Term of the loan in years.	
numMonths	Number of months for the loan.	
annualRate	Annual interest rate of the loan (as a percentage).	
monthRate	Monthly interest rate (decimal).	
loanAmount	Total amount to borrow.	
P		
Q		
monthPayment	Monthly payment.	

Step #3 – Designing a Software Solution

- It is here that we consider individual steps, or instructions, that we must implement to solve the problem.

78

Flow Chart Symbols/Types of Instructions

Symbol	Description	Symbol	Description
	Terminal - Start and End of algorithm • Only one of each (two total) per algorithm.		Conditional Statements • Always label your true and false paths!
	Assignment Statements / Expressions • Includes function calls!		Repetition Constructs • Always label your true and false paths!
	Designate Data for Input and/or Output • Don't worry about width modifiers and conversion codes.		Connector • Because paper isn't infinite in any dimension.

• **Course Standard:** For this course, only one starting and ending point (terminal) is permitted. All other implementations violate standards

Dealing with the input first:

You will notice in the C text that a descriptive prompt is not present when accepting (reading) input. It is a good idea to reference the name of the variable in the I/O symbol if it is not obvious.

• Flow charting is discussed in Appendix C of the C text. The symbols used in the C text are standard for any programming language.

• **Course Standard:** When flowcharts are a part of an assignment you MUST use a program to develop and print your charts. **No handwritten charts will be accepted.**

79

Continue with the calculations and conclude with output:

Continue with writing, saving, compiling, testing, revising…

- **Testing.** In addition to the example executions provided on all assignments you, or your group for lab assignments, should consider creating additional test cases that verify the correctness and efficiency of your solution.

- **Refinement** is an important, but often neglected, step to the problem solving process. Your first solution isn't always the best and further refinement of the algorithm might improve the efficiency of the program and eliminate any previously unobserved errors.

Chapter 2 – Introduction to the C Language

The Structure of a C Program (Figure 2-2, page 32):

Special instructions to the preprocessor that tell it how to prepare your program for compilation.

Declaration of "objects" that will be visible (usable) to all parts of the program.

- **Variables will NEVER be acceptable as global.**

The final shaded sections represent a function. A C program is made up of one or more functions, one of which must be named `main`.

- **The two sections of a function MUST not overlap!**

81

Our First Program

```
#include<stdio.h>

int main(void)
{
    printf("Hello World!\n");

    return(0);
}
```

Dissection of above program

Preprocessor Directives Section

- The only preprocessor directive statement is `#include<stdio.h>`
- This particular statement requests that a standard library (`stdio.h`) be included in order to permit the use of the standard input/output functions (such as `printf`) within the program.
- The `stdio.h` library will appear in all C programs you write this semester. Other libraries, such as `math.h`, `stdlib.h`, `cytpe.h`, and `string.h` will be introduced this semester. See Appendix F of your C programming text for a list of libraries and available functions.

Global Declarations Section

- There are no global declarations in this program.
- There will **NEVER** be global variable declarations in your program.
- The `main` function does not require a declaration and since there are no other user-defined functions, this section remains empty.

Always Remember: The **declaration section** and **execution sections** MUST NEVER overlap! You **must** complete all declarations prior to the beginning of executable statements.

Function Section

- There is only one function in this program, that function is named `main`.
- The `main` function is where execution will begin in a program.
- Every function has two distinct sections:

  1. Local Definition Section – establishes data needs for current function.
  2. Statement (Execution) Section – logic to accomplish the task of the function.

82

There are only two executable statements in the `main` function. The first statement will print the message in quotes to the screen.

- One special character `\n` included inside of the quotes will print a new line (similar to hitting the enter key on your keyboard).
- Another special character (not used in this example) `\t` is used to display a tab, but because tabs are interpreted differently it is **best to avoid** their use for a consistent appearance of your output.

The second statement is `return(0);`, this statement indicates that control of the program returns from the `main` function to the operating system, terminating the program. Later this semester we will see how the `return` statement is used to return control of the program, with or without a value, from one user-defined function to another.

More Observations from Our First Program

```
#include<stdio.h>

int main(void)
{
  printf("Hello World!\n");

  return(0);
}
```

Course Standard: All statements between the `{` and `}` are indented two spaces.

1. Notice the use of `{` and `}` that indicate the beginning `{` and end `}` of the `main` function.
   - Any C structure that has a body (the contents between the curly braces) will not terminate with a semicolon.
2. Most other C statements (and declarations) will terminate with a semicolon.
   - The rules above are good rules of thumb (that is, they usually hold true) but there will always be exceptions!

Commenting: It is reasonable to expect that a good programmer would be able to read code written by another, but sometimes the meaning of the code (and/or the thought-process of the coder) is not obvious in a logically complex segment. It is helpful if the person who wrote the code adds detailed notes in the code to assist the reader who might be a grader, tutor, fellow student, or a colleague. **Comments** are internal documentation which are ignored by the compiler and are intended to be read by another viewer of the source code.

The C programming language, any many other languages, provide two methods of commenting:

1. Single-line comments
2. Multiple-line comments

Single-line comments only span from the start of the comment to the end of the current line. A single-line comment begins with `//` and the text that follows is ignored for the remainder of the current line.

```
average = sum / numberStudents;    //CALCULATING THE EXAM AVERAGE
```

83

Multiple-line comments are used when your comments span more than one line. Instead of starting every line of code with //, we use /* to represent the start of the comment and */ to signify the end of the comment. The headers you will be required to use in all of your C programs this semester are examples of a multiple-line comment. **All text** between the /* and */ are ignored by the compiler.

```
/**********************************************************
 *
 * Programmers and Purdue Email Addresses:
 *   1. wcrum@purdue.edu
 *   2. abunning@purdue.edu
 *   3. login3@purdue.edu (delete line if no third partner)
 *
 * Lab #: 5
 *
 * Academic Integrity Statement:
 *
 * We have not used source code obtained from any other unauthorized source,
 * either modified or unmodified. Neither have we provided access to our code
 * to another. The project we are submitting is our own original work.
 *
 * Day, Time, Location of Lab: Tuesday, 9:30 - 11:20, SC 189
 *
 * Program Description: DESCRIBE YOUR ALGORITHM. WHAT DOES YOUR PROGRAM DO?
 *                      HOW DOES IT DO IT?
 *
 **********************************************************/
```

Rules regarding comments:

Note: Multiple-line comments cannot be nested.

Identifiers allow us to name data and other objects in a program.

- A piece of data used may be stored by the computer in a unique memory address, as programmers we only need to recall the identifiers we select rather than specific memory addresses to store and retrieve values from the memory of the computer.

- Every identifier will need a unique name (until chapter 4). We can use all of the letters, numbers, and the underscore to compose the name of an identifier.

Good Identifier	Bad Identifier	Documentation Standard:
numStudents	x	
depth	DEPTH	
examAvg	exam-avg	
first_lab	1st_lab	

Documentation Standard:

Rules regarding the selection of an identifier:

Types (of Data)

What is determined by a data type?

An **integer** (`int`) type is a number without a fraction part. C supports different sizes of the integer data type: `short`, `int`, `long`, and `long long`.

- The type of integer you will use depends on the data you plan to store.

`int` range, `-2147483648` to `2147483647`

Actual ranges will be system dependent.

85

A **character** (char) is any value that can be represented in the "alphabet" of the computer. Each character has a corresponding small integer value. This standard table of integer values alongside the equivalent characters is known as the **ASCII table**. You will find the ASCII table in Appendix A of the text.

- Since a character is stored in memory as an integer representing the ASCII code of a character it is possible to perform arithmetic operations on characters!

Boolean (bool) values represent logical data (either true or false). Prior to the C99 standard of the C language only integers were used to represent truth values. The compiler currently used by the course does not recognize the bool data type.

- For backward compatibility, nonzero numbers represent true and a zero value can be used to represent false.
- **We will not use the** bool **data type this semester**, an integer value can be used in its place.

A **floating point** (float) number has a fractional part, such as 3.14159. C supports different sizes (smallest to largest) of the floating point data type: float, double, and long double. The most common implementations will be double and float.

Note: Many programming references will refer to any numeric value that is not an integer as a real number. This usage may not be consistent with what you know about real and imaginary numbers from mathematics.

Variables

A **variable** is a named memory location that has a data type.

Each variable in your program must be declared and defined. In C, a declaration is used to name an object (such as a variable) and definitions are used to create the object.

- Declaration - gives the variable a name.
- Definition - reserves memory for the variable.

To create (doing both declaration and definition in one step) a variable, you first need to list the intended data type of the variable, followed by the selected identifier, and a terminal semicolon.

- int count; //COUNTS THE NUMBER OF GPAs GREATER THAN INPUT VALUE

You need to know: A variable is defined to represent a particular data type and can only store and represent values of that type!

Course Standard: Declare only a single variable per line.

Those of you with previous programming experience will know that you can create multiple variables in one statement. However, the course **programming standards** do not permit this practice. Failure to declare each variable on an individual line will result in a loss of points for a given assignment.

Variable Initialization

It is possible to **initialize** a variable at the same time it is created.

```
int count = 0;    //COURSE STANDARD - MOVE COMPLEX INITIALIZATION EXPRESSIONS TO EXECUTABLES
```

The above will initialize the space in memory reserved for the integer `count` to the value of zero. We cannot assume the memory assigned to a variable is clean (or has been cleaned) unless we initialize the variable.

- Uninitialized variables will be assigned a location in memory that may have existing data from a prior use. Such data is referred to as **garbage** because it has no predictable value for the programmer.

Constants – Literal Constants

A literal constant is an unnamed value used to specify data. For example, we want to calculate the circumference of a circle:

```
circumference = 2 * 3.14159 * radius;
```

- The values `2` and `3.14159` are both literal constants in the above expression. We may often refer to such values as being **"hard coded"** when they aren't represented symbolically (next topic).

Constants – Symbolic/Defined Constants

The `#define` preprocessor directive is used to create **symbolic constants**.

When this statement appears among the preprocessor directives, all subsequent occurrences of `symbol` will be replaced by `replacement value` automatically before the program is compiled.

Note:

Why use **symbolic/defined** constants?

- It is difficult to determine what a number represents in an arithmetic expression when the program is long and includes many complex calculations. **The use of constants helps document the program by giving meaning to operands in an expression.**

- The best reason to use constants is to make your program more **maintainable.**

  ○ For example, perhaps there are 100 students in a course. You might use the value 100 when loading data or determining the average, however, you might also use 100 to convert .853 to 85.3%. Now, what if the number of students changes to 105? You then need to search your program to determine which of those 100 values that occur in the program is related to the number of students in the course and change only those to 105.

87

Course Standard:

Symbolic Constant Examples:

Preprocessor Directive	Good or Bad Usage? Why?
`#define NUMSTU 100`	Good, clearly represents the number of students in the course.
`#define ONE 1`	Bad, vague! If the value 1 has several purposes in your program then create a constant for each!
`#define NUMBEROFEXAMS 4;`	Bad. Semi-colons are not typically used. A constant will substitute **all** values that follow the name.
`#define MaxPtsOnExam 100`	Bad, always use all upper-case letters in a symbolic constant name.

Course Standard:

Comparing Symbolic/Defined Constants with Variables:

Misapplications of Symbolic/Defined Constants

You've been asked to write a program that will be used by the data entry staff of your employer. There are only four options available; add, delete, print, and exit.

The initial solution you designed:	In the future the data entry employees asked that you rearrange the menu options as the current order of options does not match their frequency of use. The specific request is to make print the first option, add the second, and delete the third option.

```
#define ONE 1
#define TWO 2
#define THREE 3
#define FOUR 4

int main()
{
    printf("Menu options:  \n\n");
    printf("%d. Add\n", ONE);
    printf("%d. Delete\n", TWO);
    printf("%d. Print\n", THREE);
    printf("%d. Exit\n", FOUR);

    return(0);
}
```

```
#define ADD 2
#define DELETE 3
#define PRINT 1
#define EXIT 4

int main()
{
    printf("Menu options:  \n\n");
    printf("%d. Print\n", PRINT);
    printf("%d. Add\n", ADD);
    printf("%d. Delete\n", DELETE);
    printf("%d. Exit\n", EXIT);

    return(0);
}
```

- To minimize the work you must do your changes include; re-ordering the print statements in the main function and then associating each of the symbolic/defined constants with their new values.

- The third option, far right example above, would have been a better alternative. The names, symbols, or identifiers, selected for the symbolic/defined constants are meaningful in terms of what each value represents in the program rather than a description of the specific numeric value it represents.

What is in your code:	What is really being compiled on line #10:

```
3  #define APPROX_PI = 3.1415;
4
5  int main()
6  {
7      float radius = 4.25;
8      float circumference;
9
10     circumference = 2 * APPROX_PI * radius;
```

```
circumference = 2 * = 3.1415; * radius;
```

- The substitution of all that follows the symbol APPROX_PI generates an error on line #10.

- When observing an error on a line that contains a symbolic/defined constant remember that the source of the error may be in the definition at the top of your program.

I/O (Input and Output)

The `printf` function is used to display messages and data to the monitor.

- To print data the `printf` function needs two things: instructions for formatting the data and the actual data to be printed.

We saw the following in an earlier example to display text only:

- `printf ("Hello World!\n");`

It is possible to print the data represented by constants or variables in a `printf` statement:

- `printf ("The year is: %d\n", 2018);`

Where `%d` is **a placeholder** for the integer literal constant 2018.

- **Reminder:** The term **placeholder** is used here in the notes, the book will refer to the `%` as a start token to be followed by a conversion code (in the example above a "`d`" for an integer value).

The format of a `printf` statement is: `printf ( format string, data list );`

- Where the **format string** is everything inside of the double-quotes and the variables to be printed are after the comma in the **data list**.

90

You can **print all of the normal C types with** printf by using different placeholders:

- int (integer values) uses **%d**
- float (floating point values) uses **%f**
- char (single character values) uses **%c**
- **character strings** (arrays of characters, discussed later) use **%s**

A more comprehensive list of conversion codes:

Type	Size		Code	Example

Given: #define YEAR 2018

What is the output of the following?

printf("The year is YEAR.\n");

Output Generated:	

How can the value of a symbolic/defined constant be displayed within a printf **function?**

91

Width Modifiers:

- A width modifier is used with a conversion character to reserve a given amount of space for a value to be displayed.
- If the number of characters in the data to display is **less** than that specified by the width modifier then the data will be **right aligned** in the spaces reserved.

Precision Modifiers:

- A precision modifier is used with floating-point data to determine the number of digits to display to the right of the decimal point.

Placeholder Details (figure 2-18 on page 56):

Code used to generate the output on the left:

```
#include<stdio.h>

#define APPROX_PI 3.14159

int main()
{
    float radius = 4.25;
    float circumference;

    int decimalPlaces = 3;

    circumference = 2 * APPROX_PI * radius;

    printf("=============================\n");
    printf("Circumference: %18.2f\n", circumference);
    printf("Circumference: %18f\n", circumference);
    printf("Circumference: %18.*f\n", decimalPlaces, circumference);
    printf("=============================\n");

    return(0);
}
```

Example of width modifiers, precision modifiers, and variable precision modifiers:

```
=============================
Circumference:          26.70
Circumference:      26.703514
Circumference:         26.704
=============================
```

Notes on the code segment:

- The desired number of decimal places is stored in a variable named decimalPlaces.

- This value is then used to represent the desired number of decimal places to display and replaces the * in the placeholder.

- The width modifier is a fixed value of 18. This, too, could be represented by a variable similar to how it was accomplished for the precision.

The primary input function we will use this semester is called `scanf`

The format of the `scanf` function is similar to that of `printf` in that it has two sections separated by a comma.

```
scanf ( format string, address list ) ;
```

- The **format string** will list the types of data expected as input. It is possible, albeit rare, that you will read in more than one data item in a single `scanf` statement.
- The **address list** indicates where in the memory of the computer the input value should be stored.

For example:

```
printf ("Enter your age: ") ;
scanf ("%d", &age) ;
```

The user will enter an integer that will be assigned to the variable `age`.

- What about the & before `age`?
- The & is the **address operator** and refers to the address represented by the variable `age`.
- The value entered by the user will be stored in memory at the address represented by `age`.

The `scanf` function uses the same placeholders as `printf`:

- **int** uses **%d**
- **float** uses **%f**
- **char** uses **%c**
- **character strings** (discussed later) use **%s**

Remember: A \n represents a new line character for output and wouldn't be expected in a `scanf` statement.

Error Discussion

How much easier would programming be if errors did not exist? We will not be able to cover every specific error you may encounter during the term, but we will place errors in various categories today and try to mention common errors as we work our way through new topics.

Classification of errors:

1. The syntax error (at compile time)
2. The unexpected early termination of the program (crash at run-time)
3. The logical error (occurs at run-time)

Try to answer the following questions whenever you encounter an error:

1. When does the error arise?
2. What did you observe about the error?

The syntax error

You will be made aware of a syntax error when you attempt to compile your C code. It may also be said that the syntax error is a **compile-time error**. Typically, this error arises due to a mistake you made that violates the **syntax rules** of the C programming language.

- Common syntax errors include misplacing a semicolon, failing to pair all quotes, typos.

- **A warning** is an educated guess by the compiler that you have potentially made a mistake. All warnings should be remedied before you submit an assignment. If you have set up your account correctly you will be compiling utilizing the warnings option. Without this option active, you will not be made aware of any warnings.

Why are syntax errors the "best" error to observe?

Creation of Executable Files

A new executable file (a.out) will not be created when the compiler must terminate its work due to a syntax error. The keyword here is **error** and it is commonly included as part of the messages created by the compiler. If the compiler reports **only warnings** then it is likely that a new executable file (a.out) will be created. When issuing a warning the compiler has detected a potential misuse of the syntax which will often appear as a logical error as the program executes.

Example Warning Message:

```
test.c: In function 'main':
test.c:10: warning: 'ct' is used uninitialized in this function
```

The run-time errors

This is any error that occurs when the program is running. The run-time error may result in a crash. A crash is an event that causes the execution of the program to cease unexpectedly. Two very common run-time errors that result in a crash are the **segmentation fault** and the **floating exception**. Why aren't these errors detected by the compiler? The compiler may not know an attempt to divide by zero (floating exception) will occur until after the code has been compiled and the user enters a zero for a value that will then be used in the denominator of an expression.

The more difficult error to diagnose is a run-time error that does not lead to a crash! Such an error is often noticed because the output (results) is not as expected.

Logical error example, determine the average of three numbers:

```
average = x + y + z / 3;

average = (x + y + z) / 3;
```

The first statement would be syntactically correct; the statement will not cause a crash, but will result in the display of an incorrect value. The second statement is the desired result without the logical error.

- A **logical error** is a run-time error in which **the programmer is guilty** of entering a flaw in the logic of the program.

Need to know what a compiler error (or warning) message means?

1. Ask a course staff member or a classmate.
2. Try to do a Google search!

Debugging

- The process of cleaning up your errors is known as debugging. All semester we will look at various approaches to debugging your errors including:

  - Inserting **diagnostic print statements** into your code to verify the expected values at a given point in time in the execution of your program.
  - Writing small sections of code that accomplish a sub-task within the larger problem that you are trying to solve.
  - Developing test cases that represent a range of expected input.

95

Chapter 3 - Structure of a C Program

Expressions

Note:

Expression Terminology Review:

- **operator** - "language-specific syntactical token that requires an action to be taken." For example: `+`, `-`, `*`, `/`, and some others that may be new to you. If you can take one thing away from the definition above, focus on "language-specific" in that in C the operators and their meanings might be different from what you may have seen in mathematics or another programming language (namely MATLAB, Python, Excel).

- **operand** - "receives an operator's action." In other words values operated on by the operator. Depending on the operator there may be one, two, or more operands necessary to evaluate the operation.

Another idea that you should be familiar with in some form is the idea of operator **precedence**. The precedence of an operator determines the order in which it will be evaluated in an expression. The inside cover of the text book has a list of the **order of precedence** for the C language.

Printing Expression Evaluations (similar to Program 3-3 on page 103-104):	**Output:**

`int a = 17;  //FIRST OPERAND`
`int b = 5;   //SECOND OPERAND`
 	
`printf("%d + %d = %d\n", a, b, a + b);`
 	
`printf("%d / %d = %d\n", a, b, a / b);`
 	
`printf("%d %% %d = %d\n", a, b, a % b);`	

Why are there two `%s` in the format string of the third `printf`?	
Note on the modulus operator:	

96

Assignment Expressions

An assignment expression evaluates the operand on the right side of the assignment operator (=) and saves that value in the memory of the variable on the left.

Note on assignment operator:

Examples of Simple Assignment

	Course Standard:

`int x;`
`int y = 2;`
 	
`x = 3 * 4;`
`x = y * 3;`
`x = x + y;`	

Examples of Compound Assignment

- It is common to add (or apply another common mathematical operation to) a value to a variable and store that new value back to the variable.

For example, $x = x + 3$;

- Think about what is happening above in terms of memory. On the right we extract the value of x and add three to it and then store the sum back in to the memory location represented by x.

The compound assignment example:

- `x += 3;`   `//SAME AS x = x + 3;`

Compound assignment can be used with subtraction, division, multiplication, and modulus as well as with addition.

Compound Expression	Equivalent Simple Expression

Example:

```
int x = 3;
int y = 5;
int z = 7;
float a = 2.5;
float b = 5.0;

x += 4;
y /= 2;
a *= 2;
b /= 2;

z %= 4;

printf("x = %d y = %d z = %d\n", x, y, z);

printf("a = %.2f b = %.2f\n", a, b);
```

Example #2:

```
int x = 3;
int y = 5;

x /= x + y;

printf("x = %d y = %d\n", x, y);
```

Is the result x = x / x + y **or** x = x / (x + y)?

What does this tell you about the operator precedence of /= and + ?

Prefix & Post-fix Increment (and Decrement)

- You may not see the immediate need for these expressions/operations, but you will as the semester progresses! For now accept that it is very common to increase or decrease the value of a variable by 1.

A **post-fix expression** involves one operand followed by the operator.

```
int x = 0;

x++;  //POSTFIX INCREMENT
printf("The value of x is: %d\n", x);

x--; //POSTFIX DECREMENT
printf("The value of x is %d\n", x);
```

A **prefix expression** involves the operator followed by the operand.

```
int x = 0;

++x; //PREFIX INCREMENT
printf("The value of x is: %d\n", x);

--x; //PREFIX DECREMENT
printf("The value of x is %d\n", x);
```

Why are there no recognizable differences between the post-fix and prefix examples above?

- When used on a line without any other expression the post-fix and prefix operations are interchangeable.
- Additionally, under those same conditions a simple or complex assignment could be substituted for the post-fix or prefix operations.

When are the differences between the post-fix and prefix operations demonstrable?

- When those operators used as a part of another expression.

Result of Post-fix (Figure 3-3 page 96):

99

Result of Prefix (Figure 3-5 page 98):

Example to demonstrate the differences between the prefix and post-fix operations:

```
int x = 0;

printf("The value of ++x is: %d\n", ++x);

x = 0;  //RESET x

printf("The value of x++ is: %d\n", x++);
```

Note: Commands such as x = x++, or y = x++ + ++x - x-- + --x may not be interpreted the same way by different compilers. If you are warned by our compiler, find another way to do what you were hoping to accomplish.

Warning from page 114:

Mixed and Single Data Type Expressions

We have seen examples already of expression evaluations that produce results other than what we expect if we were in mathematics (or using a calculator, Excel, or MATLAB).

3 / 2 = 1

- The above example is one of those situations! What happens here in C programming is that the division of two integer values must result in another integer!

However, if we mix the types as seen the statement below:

3 + 2.1 = 5.1

The **mixed type expression** in the previous example will **implicitly type convert** the 3 to a 3.0 such that the expression is evaluated as if two floating-point values were present. Do you see any problem converting 3 to 3.0 before it is added to 2.1?

- No, there is no potential loss of data and the implicit conversion is **safe**.

From the C programming text (figure 3-10 on page 115):

What does it mean to be implicit? The computer does it for you without you, the programmer, explicitly asking for the conversion to be done!

Are there explicit data type conversions and, if so, how is an **explicit type conversion** implemented?

- **Note:** An explicit type conversion may be referred to as an **explicit cast**.

101

Example requiring an explicit type conversion:
I want to calculate `3 / 2`, but I need the answer to be `1.5`!

We saw in the mixed type expression that the integer was promoted on the hierarchy to a `float` implicitly. We can request a **cast** (type conversion) **explicitly** on one of the two operands in the division expression forcing the division to involve a floating-point and an integer. The quotient will then be stored as a floating-point value because the expression is now a mixed type expression and the second operand is changed implicitly.

$$(\texttt{float}) \ 3 \ / \ 2 \ = \ 1.5$$

Try the following:

Expression	Evaluation
`3 / (float) 2`	
`3 / 2.0`	
`(float) 3 / (float) 2`	
`(float) (3/2)`	

What do the results of the expressions above say about the precedence of the explicit cast?

Another Math Review: Rounding of numbers is a common task in problem solving. You must keep in mind the rules regarding rounding as we program this semester or better yet be able to conduct various tests to identify how rounding is taking place with your values.

- Sometimes an "extreme" form of rounding takes place called **truncation**. Truncation is removing of the entire decimal value and giving no consideration to rounding the integer that remains.
- The `floor` function (found in `math.h`, but also a commonly used function in MATLAB and Excel) will remove a remainder and reduce the number to the next smaller integer value.

Expression	Evaluation
`floor(6.99)`	
`floor(6.5)`	
`floor(6.0)`	
`floor(6.75 + 0.5)`	

Expression	Evaluation
`(int) 6.99`	
`(int) 6.5`	
`(int) 6.0`	
`(int) (6.75 + 0.5)`	

Assignment Conversions:

- This type of conversion occurs when the data type of the expression on the right-hand side of an assignment expression does not match the data type of the variable on the left-hand side of the same assignment expression.

- The result of the expression on the right hand side of the assignment expression will be converted to match that of the variable on the left-hand side. This can be interpreted as one instance when an **implicit type conversion is unsafe.**

Example - rounding and truncation

```c
int a = 3;
int c = 1;
float x = 3.99;
float y = 2.29;
float z = 8;

printf("The value of z is %f\n", z);

c = x; //ASSIGNING A FLOAT TO AN INT - ASSIGNMENT CONVERSION

printf("The value of c is %d\n", c);

printf("The value of x is %.1f and y is %.1f\n", x, y);

printf("Using mixed up placeholders: \n");
printf("x is %d and a is %f\n", x, a);

printf("Using a cast to fix placeholders: \n");
printf("x is %d and a is %f\n", (int)x, (float)a);
```

Output:

Reminder: An explicit type conversion applied to a variable WILL NOT alter the variable's data type for the remainder of a program. You can consider the type conversion is applied AFTER the data value for a variable has been retrieved from its memory.

How the value of variables are changed:

Selection via Calculation

- Wait, this is not the chapter on selection, is it? Where are the if/else if/else constructs? How can we essentially simulate selection with a calculation?

The fundamental idea here is that we can create an expression that can be activated or not based on the value of a factor which is multiplied by the expression to determine if it remains a part of the final calculation.

The factor is often a result of comparing two values to determine which of the two is larger. Given that this chapter has placed an emphasis on data types it is indeed that idea which plays a major part in the calculation of such a factor.

Example: Given two integers display the larger of the two.

```
1 #include<stdio.h>
2
3 int main()
4 {
5    int x;
6    int y;
7    int max;
8
9    printf("Enter two integers: ");
10   scanf("%d %d", &x, &y);
11
12   max = x / y * x + y / x * y;
13
14   printf("Max value input is: %d\n", max);
15
16   return(0);
17 }
```

Example Executions:

```
Enter two integers: 5 8
Max value input is: 8

Enter two integers: 9 6
Max value input is: 9

Enter two integers: 10 3
Max value input is: 30
```

- See the problem when one of the number is two or more times greater than the other?
- How do we fix this? How can we make sure that the quotients calculated are always 0 or 1?

Revision to eliminate multiplying the larger value by a factor greater than one:

```
factor1 = x / y;
factor2 = y / x;

factor1 = (factor1 + 2) % (factor1 + 1);
factor2 = (factor2 + 2) % (factor2 + 1);

max = factor1 * x + factor2 * y;
```

- Two integers factor1 and factor2 are introduced to store the values comparing x and y.
- We know the value that is zero represents the smaller of the two values and the value greater than zero is the larger.
- The modulus operator is used here to scale non-zero values to 1 while not changing the factor storing zero because 2 % 1 is zero.

Example Executions of Revised Program:

```
Enter two integers: 10 3
Max value input is: 10

Enter two integers: 8 8
Max value input is: 16
```

- We still have a problem when both integer values are the same!

104

Revision to eliminate the duplication of the output when the two values entered are the same:

```
factor1 = x / y;
factor2 = y / x;

factor1 = (factor1 + 2) % (factor1 + 1);
factor2 = (factor2 + 2) % (factor2 + 1);

max = factor1 * x + factor2 * y;

max = max / (factor1 + factor2);
```

- Only when the sum of the factors is two are both values the same. In all other cases the sum of the factors will be one.
- With that being the case we only need to divide the max by the sum of the factors to remove this unwanted doubling of the value.

Example: Using what we now know about data types and expressions, given the total number of points earned during a semester calculate (or determine) the letter grade earned.

Desired Program:

```
Enter total points earned: 470
Points Earned: 470   Grade Earned: A

Enter total points earned: 415
Points Earned: 415   Grade Earned: B

Enter total points earned: 305
Points Earned: 305   Grade Earned: D

Enter total points earned: 304
Points Earned: 304   Grade Earned: F
```

Solution:

```
#define A_MIN 470
#define B_MIN 415
#define C_MIN 360
#define D_MIN 305

int totalPoints;        //TOTAL POINTS EARNED BY STUDENT
char courseGrade;       //GRADE EARNED BY STUDENT
int gradePoints;        //4 - A, 3 - B, 2 - C, 1 - D, 0 - F

printf("Enter total points earned: ");
scanf("%d", &totalPoints);

gradePoints = totalPoints / A_MIN;
gradePoints += totalPoints / B_MIN;
gradePoints += totalPoints / C_MIN;
gradePoints += totalPoints / D_MIN;

courseGrade = 'F' - gradePoints;
courseGrade -= totalPoints / D_MIN; //TO ACCOUNT FOR 'E'

printf("Points Earned: %d   Grade Earned: %c\n", totalPoints, courseGrade);
```

105

Why use functions?

Top-Down Design

The identification of smaller tasks within the larger problem is known as **factoring** and results in small manageable sub-parts of a program to be designed and individually developed and implemented. This process of factoring tasks into more manageable parts is known as **top-down design**.

When does the factoring stop? The factoring of tasks should continue until the task "consists only of elementary processes that are intrinsically understood and cannot be further subdivided." (page 150, C Programming text)

- In simple terms, a function should consist of a **single task**. Be careful not to divide tasks such that the resulting functions are trivial. For example, the act of input of a value includes the printf, scanf, and validation of the input. To divide this task of input further would result in functions that are trivial.

When is a new function necessary?

- A function that accomplishes only a single task is known to be **functionally cohesive.** Our goal is to develop such functions and to avoid placing multiple unrelated tasks inside of the same function.

- The logic behind the task that a function accomplishes in a program should **appear only once** in the program. The motivation for this idea is that we desire to **eliminate redundant code**, that is logic which appears in more than one place in a program.

- The task that the function is completing should be **testable** by itself separate of the rest of the program.

Library Functions and Code Reuse (Reason #3 to use functions)

When writing code we want to think about the possibility of reusing that code, or part of that code, in the future. There are many tasks that are common to problems in programming and it is possible to find many of these tasks readily available (already coded) for our use through the standard libraries.

Two standard libraries we will use heavily this semester:

1. `stdio.h` - provides our standard input/out functions such as `printf` and `scanf`.
2. `math.h` - provides access to common math functions and constants such as the trigonometric functions and a precise value of pi.

The example below will calculate the third side of a triangle given the length of the other two sides and the angle in between.

```
#include<stdio.h>
#include<math.h>

#define DEGTORADIANS M_PI / 180

int main()
{
    /* LOCAL DEFINITIONS */

    float sideA;    //LENGTH OF SIDE A ENTERED BY USER
    float sideB;    //LENGTH OF SIDE B ENTERED BY USER
    float angleAB;  //ANGLE BETWEEN SIDE A AND SIDE B
    float sideC;    //LENGTH OF SIDE C TO BE CALCULATED

    /* EXECUTABLE STATEMENTS */

    printf("Enter the length of side A and side B: ");
    scanf("%f %f", &sideA, &sideB);

    printf("Enter the angle in between (in degrees): ");
    scanf("%f", &angleAB);

    angleAB = angleAB * (DEGTORADIANS);

    sideC = sqrt(pow(sideA, 2) + pow(sideB, 2) - (2 * sideA * sideB * cos(angleAB)));

    printf("The length of the third side is %.2f\n", sideC);

    return(0);
}
```

- **Notice the function calls and use of the M_PI constant from the math.h library.**

Basic Function Terminology

Behind ALL WELL-WRITTEN programs is the same fundamental element, the function. The function will be the implementation and contain the solution of the single sub-task previously described.

What is a function? According to the Gilberg and Forouzan text, "A named block of code, consisting of a header, function name, and a body, that is designed to perform a task within the program."

- When the services of a function are requested it must be **called**. The function making the call is known as the **calling function** and the function being called is the **called function**.
- It is common that data needs to be exchanged between the calling and called functions.

    - The technique of sending (passing) data to a function is known as **parameter passing.**
    - It is possible that the function may complete a calculation and wish to share the result with the calling function. We often refer to this as **returning** a value from a function.
    - In C Programming, a function is only capable of **returning at most one value.**

In **figure 4-5 (page 155)** we observe a `main` function that contains two statements, one statement is a **call** to a function named (identified as) `greeting` and the second statement is the terminal return (`return 0;`) statement. When the function `greeting` is called by `main` control of the program leaves `main`. The function `greeting` will execute its two statements which will print `Hello World!` to the monitor and then return control of the program to the calling function `main`. The `main` function will continue from where it left off following the function call, in this case, `main`'s next statement will be the terminal `return (0)` statement.

- The **sequence** of which **instructions are executed** in the program now jumps from `main` to `greeting` when the function is called.
- It is "remembered" where in `main` the function call was made so that when the called function (`greeting`) terminates the execution of statements in `main` will continue with the statement following the function call.

Important Note: When a called function terminates the program will continue with the statement that follows the call statement in the calling function.

108

User-Defined Functions

As with variables, functions must be both **declared** and **defined**.

- The function declaration will appear in the global declaration section of the program.

What is the compiler looking for?

- All three components of a user-defined function, (declaration, definition, and call) are in agreement.

What is the error generated when the definition cannot be found?

What is the error generated when the declaration cannot be found?

The function declaration statement will tell the compiler...

- The **function definition** contains the code needed to complete the task.

Basic Function Designs

	Yes Parameters	No Parameters
Yes Value Returned		
No Value Returned		

1. A function with no parameters that returns no value.
2. A function with no parameters that returns a value.
3. A function with parameters that returns a value.
4. A function with parameters that returns no value.

What is "void" about a void **function?**

Which categories are considered void **functions?**

A Function with no Parameters that Returns no Value

- The greeting function above is an example of a **void function** (sometimes called procedures) and are useful to handle tasks that require no value to be returned.

```
/* GLOBAL DECLARATIONS */

void welcome(void);   //FUNCTION DECLARATION

int main()
{
    /* EXECUTABLE STATEMENTS */
    welcome();   //FUNCTION CALL

    return(0);

}

/*******************************************************************
 *
 * Function Information
 *
 * Name of Function: welcome
 *
 * Function Return Type: void
 *
 * Parameters (list data type, name, and comment one per line) : None
 *
 * Function Description:  This function prints a welcome message to the user.
 *
 *******************************************************************/
void welcome()
{
    printf("\n\nWelcome to the function demonstration program!  In this\n");
    printf("program we will demonstrate the four category of functions\n");
    printf("described in the notes.\n\n");

}
```

Course Standard: Use a course header (head_fx) for each user-defined function. The main function does not require a header. The assignment header will act as the header for main.

110

A Function with no Parameters that Returns a Value

- Input functions are a good example of the category of functions which accept no data into the function but is able to generate and return a single value.

```
#include<stdio.h>

/* GLOBAL DECLARATIONS */

void welcome(void);
int operandInput(void);

int main()
{
    /* LOCAL DECLARATIONS */
    int op1;   //OPERAND #1
    int op2;   //OPERAND #2

    /* EXECUTABLE STATEMENTS */
    welcome();

    op1 = operandInput();
    op2 = operandInput();

    return(0);

}
```

Figure 4-7 (page 158) is another example of a non-void function without parameters:

111

Adding the definition of the input function to our work in progress:

```
/********************************************************************
 *
 *   Function Information
 *
 *   Name of Function: operandInput
 *
 *   Function Return Type: int
 *
 *   Parameters (list data type, name, and comment one per line): None
 *
 *   Function Description: This function will accept and return input from user.
 *
 *******************************************************************/
int operandInput()
{
    int operand;   //USER'S OPERAND INPUT

    printf("Enter the operand value: ");
    scanf("%d", &operand);

    return(operand);
}

//FUNCTION HEADER REMOVED FROM THIS FUNCTION TO SAVE SPACE

void welcome()
{
    printf("\n\nWelcome to the function demonstration program!  In this\n");
    printf("program we will demonstrate the four category of functions\n");
    printf("described in the notes.\n\n");

    return;   //RETURN IN A VOID FUNCTION IS OPTIONAL
}
```

Observations:

- The value input by the user is returned to the calling function and completes the assignment expression back in main.
- Notice the function declaration lists a return type of int and the lack of parameters indicated by empty parentheses.

112

A Function with Arguments that Returns a Value

```c
#include<stdio.h>

/* GLOBAL DECLARATIONS */

void welcome(void);
int operandInput(void);
int calculateRemainder(int, int);
int integerDivision(int, int);

int main()
{
    /* LOCAL DECLARATIONS */

    int op1; //OPERAND #1
    int op2; //OPERAND #2
    int remainder; //HOLDS THE RESULT OF THE REMAINDER
    int quotient; //HOLDS THE RESULT OF INT DIVISION

    /* EXECUTABLE STATEMENTS */

    welcome();

    op1 = operandInput();
    op2 = operandInput();

    remainder = calculateRemainder(op1, op2);
    quotient = integerDivision(op1, op2);

    return(0);

}

void welcome()
{
    printf("\n\nWelcome to the function demonstration program! In this\n");
    printf("program we will demonstrate the four category of functions\n");
    printf("described in the notes.\n\n");
}
```

```
/*******************************************************************
 *
 *   Function Information
 *
 *   Name of Function: integerDivision
 *
 *   Function Return Type: ubt
 *
 *   Parameters (list data type, name, and comment one per line):
 *     1. int x //FIRST OPERAND FOR QUOTIENT CALCULATION
 *     2. int y //SECOND OPERAND FOR QUOTIENT CALCULATION
 *
 *   Function Description: Calculates the quotient of two integer values.
 *
 *******************************************************************/
int integerDivision(int x, int y)
{
    return(x / y);
}

int operandInput()
{
    /* LOCAL DECARATIONS */

    int operand;   //USER'S OPERAND INPUT

    /* EXECUTABLE STATEMENTS */

    printf("Enter the operand value: ");
    scanf("%d", &operand);

    return(operand);
}
```

Note: The identifiers for the parameters in both the integerDivision and calculateRemainder **(next page)** function defintions are the same. **What is the relationship between these variables? Is the relationship dependent on the shared identifiers?**

114

```
/****************************************************************
 *
 *   Function Information
 *
 *   Name of Function: calculateRemainder
 *
 *   Function Return Type: int
 *
 *   Parameters (list data type, name, and comment one per line):
 *      1. int x // FIRST OPERAND FOR REMAINDER CALCULATION
 *      2. int y // SECOND OPERAND FOR REMAINDER CALCULATION
 *
 *   Function Description: Calculates the remainder of two integer values.
 *
 ****************************************************************/
int calculateRemainder(int x, int y)
{
    /* LOCAL DECLARATIONS */

    int remain;  //WILL HOLD THE RESULT OF x % y

    /* EXECUTABLE STATEMENTS */

    remain = x % y;

    return(remain);

}
```

Note: Local declarations (remain variable in the function definition above) are still commented to the right and will NOT be included with the parameters in the function assignment header.

Observations:

- In calculateRemainder a new local variable is created to store the value of the modulus operator then the value of the variable is returned.
- In the integerDivision function the result of the expression is returned and is not stored locally in the function.
- The order in which functions are listed (defined) does not matter [as we will utilize such functions this semester]. **However,** main **should come first!!**

115

A Function with Arguments that Returns no Value (void)

- **Reminder:** A function is **void** if it returns no value. The term "void function" says nothing about parameters, but only the lack of a value returned.

	Note on identifiers in function declarations:

```/* GLOBAL DECLARATIONS */```
 	
```void welcome(void);```
```int operandInput(void);```
```int calculateRemainder(int, int);```
```int integerDivision(int, int);```
```void displayResults(int op1, int op2, int quo, int rem);```	

```int main()```
```{```
 	
   ```/* LOCAL DECLARATIONS */```
 	
   ```int op1; //OPERAND #1```
   ```int op2; //OPERAND #2```
   ```int remainder; //HOLDS THE RESULT OF THE REMAINDER```
   ```int quotient; //HOLDS THE RESULT OF INT DIVISION```
 	
   ```/* EXECTUABLE STATEMENTS */```
 	
   ```welcome();```
 	
   ```op1 = operandInput();```
   ```op2 = operandInput();```
 	
   ```remainder = calculateRemainder(op1, op2);```
   ```quotient = integerDivision(op1, op2);```
 	
   ```displayResults(op1, op2, quotient, remainder);```
 	
   ```return(0);```
 	
```}```
	Observations about ```main``` **function:**

```
int integerDivision(int x, int y)
{
  return(x / y);
}
```

```
int calculateRemainder(int x, int y)
{
    /* LOCAL DECLARATIONS */

    int remain;  //WILL HOLD THE RESULT OF x % y

    /* EXECUTABLE STATEMENTS */

    remain = x % y;

    return(remain);
}

/*****************************************************************
*
*  Function Information
*
*  Name of Function: displayResults
*
*  Function Return Type: void
*
*  Parameters (list data type, name, and comment one per line):
*      1. int op1        // FIRST OPERAND FOR CALCULATIONS AS ENTERED BY USER
*      2. int op2        // SECOND OPERAND FOR CALCULATIONS AS ENTERED BY USER
*      3. int quo        // QUOTIENT OF TWO INTEGER OPERANDS ABOVE
*      4. int reminader  // REMAINDER OF TWO INTEGER OPERANDS ABOVE
*
*  Function Description:  Displays the final output as required by program.
*
*****************************************************************/
void displayResults(int op1, int op2, int quo, int remainder)
{
    /* EXECUTABLE STATEMENTS */

    printf("\n\n");
    printf("%d / %d = %d\n\n", op1, op2, quo);
    printf("%d %% %d = %d\n\n", op1, op2, remainder);
}
```

Description of logical error created during lecture with the parameters in the function call and function definition:

117

```
int operandInput()
{
    /* LOCAL DECLARATIONS */

    int operand;  //USER'S OPERAND INPUT

    /* EXECUTABLE STATEMENTS */

    printf("Enter the operand value: ");
    scanf("%d", &operand);
    return(operand);
}

void welcome()
{
    /* EXECTUABLE STATEMENTS */

    printf("\n\nWelcome to the function demonstration program!  In this\n");
    printf("program we will demonstrate the four category of functions\n");
    printf("described in the notes.\n\n");
}
```

Observations:

- Only the new displayResults function definition is included with its header to save space in the notes. Each and every one of your user-defined functions must include a completed course function header!

- Notice the declaration of this new function. Between the parentheses the type and number of the arguments for the function are listed.

- The number, type, and order of the parameters are important! But any parameter names (identifiers) found in a function declaration are optional and meaningless.

CRITICAL PROGRAMMING STANDARD - From the course standards.

With our ability to implement user-defined functions **only the following will be permitted** in the main function:

1. Declaration of variables to be passed to functions.
2. Calls to user-defined functions by main.
3. A limited amount of control structures (see chapters 5 and 6) to retain the previous two tasks within the main function.

Additionally, each user-defined function may represent a single task in your larger program. The failure to make a good use of user-defined function as described here and in the course standards will result in a loss of ALL points on those assignments that require user-defined functions.

Single-use functions compared with multiple-use functions:

| ```c
int main()
{
    int x = 3;
    int y = 5;
    int z;

    z = add(x, y);

    return(0);

}

int add(int x, int y)
{
    return(x + y);

}
``` | ```c
int main()
{
    int x = 3;
    int y = 5;
    int z;
    int a = 11;
    int b = 7;
    int c;

    z = add(x, y);
    c = add2(a, b);

    return(0);

}

int add(int x, int y)
{
    return(x + y);

}

int add2(int a, int b)
{
    return(a + b);

}
``` |

What if two new variables were introduced in the `main` **function on the left and those two variables (**`a` **and** `b`**) needed to be added?**

Does it makes sense to write a function similar to that of `add2` **just so the identifiers of all variables involved can match?**

Or, can the original `add` **function be used again by passing** `a` **and** `b`**?**

Parameter Passing

When we send data to a function what is happening in memory of the computer?

The two possibilities are:

1. The values of the variables passed are being sent to the function and in the function new variables with new memory locations are created to store what is essentially a **copy of the values**.
2. The variables in the called function are linked to the variables in the calling function such that they **share memory** and changes to the values in the called function will be changes to the variables in the calling function.

119

Output Generated:

```
void exchangeValues(int, int);

int main()
{
    int x = 3;
    int y = 5;

    printf("Before the function: x = %d y = %d\n", x, y);

    exchangeValues(x, y);

    printf("After the function: x = %d y = %d\n", x, y);

    return(0);
}

void exchangeValues(int a, int b)
{
    int temp;

    printf("Before the exchange: a = %d b = %d\n", a, b);

    temp = a;
    a = b;
    b = temp;

    printf("After the exchange: a = %d b = %d\n", a, b);
}
```

- If possibility #1 is true, then changing a will not change x as evidenced by the final print statement in main.
- If is possibility #2, then upon changing the variable a in the called function we will observe the variable x being changed when control is returned to main.

120

When copies of values of variables are passed to functions it is called a **pass by value (downward communication)**.

In **figure 4-18 (page 177)** you can see that the value of a is passed to the function where it is stored in the memory location represented by the local variable x.

- Changes to x will be independent of the variable a in the calling function.

What roles do the identifiers of the variables in the calling and called function play in the pass by value paradigm?

Pass by Value (downward communication) versus Pass by Address (upward communication)

A few questions that you should be pondering at this point are:

1. Is it ever possible to "return" more than one value from a function?
2. Are there are alternatives to pass by value?

The answer to both questions is YES and involves the same idea. What we need to be able to do is not pass a copy of the value of a parameter, but rather to make a connection between a variable in the called function to a variable in the calling function. To do this, we must **pass the memory address of the variable** to a function rather than passing a copy of that variable's value. By passing the memory address of a variable in the calling function to the called function we can now make changes to the contents of that memory address and making any such changes is permanent (available to the calling function after the called function terminates).

To use pass by address we need to know a little bit about **pointers**. We will cover pointers in detail in chapters 9 and 10, but using them to accomplish pass by address will benefit us now.

Figure 4-20 (page 179) demonstrates how pass by address can be used to alter the value of a parameter such that when the function terminates the changed value is observed back in the calling function.

Pointer Operations

- To pass the address of a single variable we use the address (&) operator before the name of that variable. This is seen in the function calls of the previous example.

- A **pointer** is a variable that **stores the memory address** of another variable as its value. Hence, we need such a variable to receive the address being sent from the calling function to the called function.

  o In the example from figure 4-20 of the C programming text, the integer pointer `ax` in the function called `upFun` will store the memory address of the integer variable `a` in `main`.

- Now that `ax` references the memory address of `a` any change to a via `ax` must be done by making use of the indirection (or dereference) operator `*`. Notice how the value to which `ax` references (a) is being changed from within the `upFun` function.

Example: Write a program that accepts the addresses two integer variables as parameters and swaps the values between the two variables. These changes need to be available in the calling function.

- Here we have a function, `exchangeValues`, with a single task (swap two values) that needs to make available to its calling function changes to more than one variable and those changes need to be available back in the calling function.

- The task of input also makes use of passing by address. This may not be the best use of pass-by-address as logic will be added to input functions in later chapters. These pending additions will make the input function for multiple variables unnecessarily long and complex when using pass-by-address.

```
void exchangeValues(int*, int*);
void getInput(int*, int*);

int main()
{
    int a = 17;
    int b = 5;

    printf("Before a = %d b = %d\n", a, b);

    getInput(&a, &b);
    exchangeValues(&a, &b);

    printf("After a = %d b = %d\n", a, b);

    return(0);
}
```

```
void exchangeValues(int *x, int *y)
{
    int temp;

    printf("Before exchange x = %d y = %d\n", *x, *y);

    temp = *x;
    *x = *y;
    *y = temp;

    printf("After exchange x = %d y = %d\n", *x, *y);
}

void getInput(int *ax, int *ay)
{
    printf("Enter the first value: ");
    scanf("%d", ax);

    printf("Enter the second value: ");
    scanf("%d", ay);
}
```

123

Note: A function that makes use of **pass by address** does NOT have to be `void`, a value still can be returned through the use of the keyword `return`. Neither is such a function required to accept all parameters by address.

Question: Why is the address operator (&) not used before the variables in the `scanf`?

Describe the three assignment statement expressions between the two print statements in the `exchangeValues` function:

When to use pass by address?

Scope determines the region of the program in which a defined object is visible - that is, the part of the program in which you can use an object's name. Can two objects have the same name? The answer is yes, if the **scope** of each object does not overlap!

124

Example (indicate the scope of getRadius, the variables in main, and the variables in getRadius):

```
float getRadius();

int main()
{
    float radius;    //RADIUS OF CIRCLE TO BE INPUT
    float area;      //AREA OF CIRCLE TO BE CALCULATED

    radius = getRadius();

    area = M_PI * radius * radius;

    printf("The area is: %.2f\n", area);

    return(0);
}

float getRadius()
{
    float radius;    //RADIUS OF CIRCLE

    printf("Enter the value of the radius: ");
    scanf("%f", &radius);

    return(radius);
}
```

What is the scope of the user-defined functions?

* The scope of all user-defined functions we write this semester will be **global**. A **global scope** means anywhere in the program the object can be accessed or utilized.

What is the scope of the variables?

* Every variable in this program has a **local scope**, that is, the variables can only be referenced from within the function they have been declared.

Course standards require all variables this semester to have a local scope. The use of variables will global scope will result in a ZERO for an assignment if such as use is intended to circumvent the passing of parameters and the return of values from a user-defined function.

125

Documentation & Programming Standards Reminders:

- Not all documentation standards are followed in the examples found within the notes, this is done to save space. All assignments include remainders of numerous standards and refer you back to the standards document found in this packet.

1. Indent two spaces all code found within a function.
2. Do not permit location declarations and executable statements to overlap.
3. All variables must be commented in all functions.
4. All functions must make use of the course function header.
5. Comment all parameters in the function header, one per line.
6. The `main` function must be limited in its contents, factor all tasks into functions.
   - Establish your data needs via variable declarations in `main`.
   - Retain a majority of the function calls in `main`.
   - Factor all sub-tasks of the program to user-defined functions.

Structure Charts

A **structure chart** is the primary design tool for a program. You should complete your structure chart for a program before you attempt to develop any flowcharts (or write any code). A structure chart will represent each function that is present in your program and the order in which they are called. You can next create a flowchart for each function after your structure chart is complete.

Structure Chart Rules and Symbols

The two symbols to the left are used to indicate function calls. The first symbol will represent a function called a single time in a program. The name of the function will go inside of the box.

The second symbol contains a "cross-hatch" in the lower-right corner. All functions listed with such a cross-hatch indicate that it is called more than once in the program. To limit the number of sub-functions in a structure chart you only need to list the sub-functions called by this particular function one time (the first time it is used).

How to Read a Structure Chart

Structure charts are read top-down and then left-right. The book is inconsistent when it comes to what should be in the top-most box, we will recommend that this box be a representation of the `main` function.

- A structure chart shows only function (and perhaps data) flow, it will contain no code!

The following is a summary of the basic **structure chart rules** (page 210):

126

You may find it helpful in certain circumstances to list the values going into and out from a user-defined function. The symbols on the left can be used to designate such values going in and out of a function. Variables **sent to a function should be listed to the left** of the line and those **coming out of a function on the right.**

Structure Chart from calculator problem demonstrated in the notes:

How does the design of the above structure chart represent the expectation regarding the role of the `main` **function in a well-designed program?**

- In general, the structure charts are more horizontal (wide) than they are vertical (deep). This indicates that most, if not all, of the user-defined functions should be called from within the `main` function.

- As mentioned previously, every user-defined function should be limited to completing a single task of the larger problem which your program is designed to solve.

Flawed Design #2:

Concerns with the above design:

Flawed Design #1:

Concerns with the above design:

Resist the Urge to Code!

Introduction to Problem Solving Techniques

Computer Science's Method to Solving Problems

1. **Specify what is desired of the program.**
   - In an introductory programming course the specifications are given to you by the instructor assigning the problem.
   - In the real world you would meet with fellow engineers, scientists, supervisors, and/or clients to determine how and what the software must successfully accomplish.
   - **Recommendation:** Get experience working in this area before you graduate from college. Try programs such as EPICS, ENTR, and professional experiences.

2. **Analyze the problem.**
   - Factor the tasks as specified by top-down design making use of tools such as **structure charts.**
   - This step requires the development of the mathematical formulas necessary to solve the problem. Some formulas are very common such as determining the slope of a line, the distance between two points, the length of the hypotenuse of a right triangle, but other formulas are advanced and specific to your engineering or scientific discipline.
   - Once you have determined the arithmetic expressions necessary to solve the problem, be mindful to consider potential errors that may arise. Examples include dividing by zero or dealing with negative values where such is impossible (number of people, certain measures of distance and time). **Through planning you begin to work out potential errors in your logic.**

3. **Design the software solution.**
   - The flow chart or pseudo-code representation of the algorithm is developed at this point in the process. Both flowcharting and pseudo-coding are techniques you can use to design your algorithm to solve the problem at hand.
   - **Application:** When working with teams be sure to represent your logic visually so others can see what you are thinking as you present an idea for a solution.
   - As our ability to solve problems becomes more advanced be sure to design the solution to each task individually. When you have all of the tasks designed the problem of re-assembling the tasks to a final solution is simple to complete.

4. **Translate the design into code.**
   - Code only small portions of the solution (at most one task at a time).
   - Test each and every change you make!
   - Never write an entire program before you (compile and) test for the first time!
   - **Benefit:** Investing time in the previous steps in the process can really make this step: (1) shorter in terms of time and (2) a lot less frustrating.

5. **Test and debug the implementation.**
   - When testing, be sure to develop test cases and expected output that go beyond those provided on the assignment.
   - What tests have you run to ensure that your program handles all reasonable input?
   - General cases, boundary cases, extreme/stress cases.

6. **Refinement of the solution.**
   - Congratulations, you have a solution! Now, review your solution and make sure it is efficient, well-designed, meets all requirements, produces no warnings or syntax errors, and satisfies all course documentation and programming standards. **Your first solution is rarely the best solution. Make every effort to refine your algorithm so that it makes the best possible use of the limited resources of the computer.**

Structured Programming – What is it?

- There are three fundamental ideas in structured programming; selection, repetition, and sequence.

- **Sequence** was the topic of chapter 4 (user-defined functions). The use of functions permit the individual instructions of a program to be executed in an order other than first statement to the last statement and some statements may be executed more than once.

- **Selection** is the topic of chapter 5. Selection constructs will allow instructions to be executed based on a given criteria and other instructions to be excluded. This is the first point in the semester where not all code in a program may be executed in each test case.

- **Repetition** is the topic of chapter 6. Often a set of instructions needs to be repeated while a particular condition is met, or until a condition is met. Repetition constructs allow the use of logic to specify conditions and those instructs to repeat.

Chapter 5 - Selection

While functions permit us to modularize code and shift control (alter **sequence** of code executed) between functions to accomplish individual tasks, what we need next are the abilities to **select** and **repeat** code. It is **selection** that is the topic of chapter 5.

Up to this point in the course we have always observed all statements in a program being executed at least one time.

- While user-defined functions allow us to alter the sequence at this point in the course when we make a function call all of the code in that function is executed.

- The idea of selection involves selecting code to execute or exclude based on a condition.

Logical Data

A piece of data is called **logical** if it conveys the value of true or false. Logical data is generated by a **logical expression**. Logical expressions are utilized in both selection and repetition constructs. The C programming language did not traditionally have a data type specifically for logical data and instead would utilize a numeric type to represent true and false.

Note:

Figure 5-1 (page 232):

130

Logical Operators

There are three main logical operators. Logical operators are used to for combining logical values.

Operator	Character(s)	Description	Precedence

Logical Operators Truth Table (Figure 5-2, page 233):

not			and			or		
x	!x		x	y	x && y	x	y	x || y

Evaluating Logical Expressions

- That is, evaluating expressions that contain logical operators.

There are two potential approaches to evaluating such expressions:

- How can we evaluate an expression prior to evaluating every component of the expression? You wouldn't assign a value to many mathematical expressions without evaluating every operation.

As soon as it is determined that the logical expression is true or false the evaluating of remaining logical expressions stops (or **short-circuits**).

131

The short-circuit method (Figure 5-3, page 234):

	Output:
Example (similar to) Program 5-1 from text:	
`int a = 1;`	
`int b = -1;`	
`int c = 0;`	
	1.
	2.
`printf("%2d && %2d = %2d\n", a, b, a && b);`	
`printf("%2d && %2d = %2d\n", a, c, a && c);`	**3.**
	4.
`printf("%2d || %2d = %2d\n", a, b, a || b);`	
`printf("%2d || %2d = %2d\n", a, c, a || c);`	**5.**
	6.
`printf("%2d && %2d = %2d\n", a, !c, a && !c);`	
`printf("%2d || %2d = %2d\n", !a, c, !a || c);`	**7.**
	8.
`printf("--a !c = %2d\n", --a && !c);`	
`printf("b++ || ++c = %2d\n", b++ || ++c);`	**9.**
`printf("a = %d b = %d c = %d\n", a, b, c);`	

Why do we observe the values we do for the final print statement in the code segment above?

Relational (Comparative) Operators

There are six relational operators found in the C programming language. All of these operators are binary operators in which two operands are evaluated. **The result of a relational expression is a logical (0, 1) value.**

Relational Operators (figure 5-4, page 236):

Type	Operator	Meaning	Precedence

Compound Statements

It is possible to string together a series of relational and logical operators to form what is called a **compound statement.** The result of such a statement (or expression) will be a (true or false) logical value.

Examples of compound statement:

- `x > 0 && x < 10`

Often a compound statement is made easier to read by including parentheses. Can you determine which of the expressions below is different than the other two?

Example:

```
int x = 3;
int y = 2;
int z = 3;

printf("Result #1 = %d\n",  x <= 3 || y >= 2 && z != 3);
printf("Result #2 = %d\n",  x <= 3 || (y >= 2 && z != 3));
printf("Result #3 = %d\n",  (x <= 3 || y >= 2) && z != 3);
```

133

Note: Our compiler will issue a warning suggesting that you make use of (and) when using && and || in the same expression.

Another example:

```
int x = 3;
int y = 2;
int z = 3;

printf("Result #1 = %d\n", x++ <= 3 || y++ >= 2 && z++ != 3);

printf("x: %d y: %d z: %d\n", x, y, z);
```

What is the output of the above program?

What is operator binding? How is this related to precedence?

How is it evaluated?

Example:

```
int x = 7;
int y = 9;
int z = 5;

int result;

result = !(++y - 9) || -5 + z++ && x++;

printf("x: %d y: %d z: %d\n", x, y, z);
```

Complements

Each of the six relational operators is a complement of another operator. Whenever one logical expression is true its complement would be false. Whenever one logical expression is false its complement would be true.

- For example, `x < 3` represents all numbers less than 3, the complement `x >= 3` represents all other values.

Copy figure 5-5 (page 236) below:

	Complementing the Logical Operators (see DeMorgan's Rule on pages 241 – 242 of the C text):

Original Expression:	**Complement:**
`x > 0 && x < 10`	
`x > 0 && x < 10 || y != 0`	
`!(x != 1 && x != 2)`	Complement #1:
	Complement #2:
`!x && !y`	Complement #1:
	Complement #2:
`x == 0 || y == 0`	Complement #1:
	Complement #2:

135

Selection Flowchart Example #1:

Ask the user for their exam score and based on their score let them know what grade they earned (A, B, C, D, F based on 90, 80, 70, 60) and give them an appropriate message of congratulations (or not).

Step #1 – What is specified of the program?

- Input – A single score.
- Output – A message related to the grade earned and the grade earned.

Step #2 – Analyze the problem

- Structure chart representing the user-defined functions of this problem.

Step #3 – The Software Solution

- **Main function**

- **First user-defined function – accept input**

- **Second user-defined function – determine grade**

- **Third user-defined function – print relevant message**

- **Fourth user-defined function – print final grade**

- **Note:** In general it is best to eliminate any code that is common to more than one path in a selection construct. Such code should ideally be found before or after the selection construct. Every path in a selection construct should contain statements that are unique to that particular condition.

Two-Way Selection

- Logical expressions evaluate to either a true or false value.
- If the resulting logical value is true we have one path to travel, but if the result is false we will execute alternative (and unique) statements found down the alternative path.
- Two selection constructs are available for two-way selection: **if…else** and the **conditional expression**.

If…Else

- One implementation of two way selection is the if…else construct.

```
if (logical expression)
{

    //ONE OR MORE STATEMENTS

}
else
{

    //ONE OR MORE STATEMENTS

}
```

- If the first condition (logical expression) listed is evaluated to be true the statements found in the body of the if will be executed, otherwise execute the statements found in the body of the else.

Figure 5-6 (page 238) illustrates the two-way decision logic:

138

Example: if a number is even add one to make it odd, if a number is odd subtract one to make it even.

```
int changeNumber(int n)
{
    if(n % 2 == 0)
    {
        n++;
    }
    else
    {
        n--;
    }

    return(n);
}
```

Example #2: Revise the previous program to only change the value (subtract one) if odd.

```
int changeNumber(int n)
{
    if(n % 2 == 1)
    {
        n--;
    }
    else
    {
        //WHY AM I HERE, I SERVE NO PURPOSE!?!
    }

    return(n);
}
```

```
int changeNumber(int n)
{
    if(n % 2 == 0)
    {
        //NO! BAD!    NEVER SHOULD BE EMPTY!!
    }
    else
    {
        n--;
    }

    return(n);
}
```

Best solution option for problem (else **is optional**):

```
int changeNumber(int n)
{
    if(n % 2 == 1)
    {
        n--;
    }

    return(n);
}
```

139

Nested Selection

The if/else can contain any executable statement, including another if/else construct. When this occurs we call it **nested selection**. Often, nested selection involves the comparison of two (or more) different variables.

Logical Flow of Nested Selection (figure 5-13, page 243):	**Code example of nested selection:**
| | ```
int calcStatus(float gpa, int credit_hrs)
{
    int status;

    if(credit_hrs > 120)
    {
        if(gpa >= 3.50)
        {
            status = HONORS;
        }
        else
        {
            status = CANDIDATE;
        }
    }
    else
    {
        status = NONCANDIDATE;
    }
    return(status);
}
``` |

Dangling Else Logical Error and Nested if/else

- **Debugging Concern:** Please note that the text (and probably many other sources) will not always use { } with if/else statements that contain only a single statement in their body. However, this can lead to a difficult to logical problem known as the "dangling else".

- Because this problem can be so difficult to debug, **we will require ALL if/else statements to use { } even if the body contains only a single executable statement.**

140
```

Example of dangling else logical error:

	Output Generated:
| ```c
int x = 3;
int y = 2;
int z = 0;

if(x == 3)
    if(y != 2)
        z++;
    else
        z--;

printf("z = %d\n", z);
``` | |

Logic interpretation of code above (figure 5-14, page 245):
```

Conditional Expressions

The conditional expression has three operands and two operators. Each operand is itself an expression.

- The first operator is a question mark that separates the first two expressions.
- The second operator is a colon and separates the last two expressions.

To evaluate a conditional expression, we first must evaluate the leftmost expression. If that expression is true, then the value of the second expression (the first expression after the `?`) is evaluated. However, if the first expression (before the `?`) is false, then the final expression is evaluated.

- Can you see the similarities here between the `if`/`else` and the conditional expression?
- The conditional expression makes for a nice shortcut for two-way selection.

Figure 5-16 (page 247) is a sample conditional expression. If `a` is equal to `b` then increment `c` by 1, else, increment `d` by 1:

More Conditional Expression Examples:

	Output Generated:
```int a = 1;```	
```int b = -1;```	
```int c;```	
```c = a > b ? 1 : 2;```	
```printf("c = %d\n", c);```	
```a == b ? printf("a == b\n") : printf("a != b\n");```	

142

Multi-way Selection

It is a common problem to require selection from more than two alternative sections of unique code. This is the idea of multi-way selection.

- In C, there are two different constructs available to implement multi-way selection. The first is by using if/else if/else technique, the second is a switch construct. The switch construct has a few more restrictions than the if/else if/else construct but the switch may be useful when the expression tested always evaluates to an integer.

Multi-way Selection if/else if/else

- **Example:** Write a program that will accept a score as input and reply to the user based on the score what letter grade they can expect to receive.

```
#define MINA 90
#define MINB 80
#define MINC 70
#define MIND 60

int getScore();
char determineGrade(int);
void displayResults(char, int);
```

```
int main()
{
    int score;    //SCORE OF STUDENT
    char grade;   //CALCULATED GRADE BASED ON SCORE

    score = getScore();
    grade = determineGrade(score);

    displayResults(grade, score);

    return(0);
}
```

```
void displayResults(char grade, int score)
{
    printf("Based on your score of %d, you will receive the grade of %c in this course.\n", score, grade);
}
```

```
int getScore()
{
    int score;   //SCORE TO BE ENTERED BY THE USER

    printf("Enter the score for the course: ");
    scanf("%d", &score);

    return(score);
}
```

Figure 5-24 on page 261 is a good flowchart illustration of this selection construct.

```
char determineGrade(int score)
{
    char grade;

    if(score >= MINA)
    {
        grade = 'A';
    }
    else if(score >= MINB)
    {
        grade = 'B';
    }
    else if(score >= MINC)
    {
        grade = 'C';
    }
    else if(score >= MIND)
    {
        grade = 'D';
    }
    else
    {
        grade = 'F';
    }
    return(grade);
}
```

Note: In this example as soon as one of the conditions is true the statements in the body for the particular condition are executed and then the if/else if/else structure is exited.

Are either of the constructs below logically equivalent to the one on the previous page?

```
if(score >= MINA)
{
    grade = 'A';
}
else if(score >= MINB && score < MINA)
{
    grade = 'B';
}
else if(score >= MINC && score < MINB)
{
    grade = 'C';
}
else if(score >= MIND && score < MINC)
{
    grade = 'D';
}
else
{
    grade = 'F';
}
```

```
if(score >= MINA)
{
    grade = 'A';
}
if(score >= MINB && score < MINA)
{
    grade = 'B';
}
if(score >= MINC && score < MINB)
{
    grade = 'C';
}
if(score >= MIND && score < MINC)
{
    grade = 'D';
}
else
{
    grade = 'F';
}
```

Flowchart for code segment above on the right:

145

Multi-way Selection switch

A switch construct is used to make a selection among many possible integer value alternatives.

The **control expression** is evaluated and selected upon by comparing it to a series of cases. For every possible value that can result from the condition, a separate case is defined.

- Each case can have zero **or more** executable statements.
- There should exist one or more possible cases. You should consider an if/else if when the number of cases is large.
- A default case may exist, consider this idea similar to an else statement in an if construct.

Note: Each case is compared with the value of the control expression for equality.

```
void displayResults(char grade, int score)
{
    printf("Based on your score of %d, you will receive the grade of %c in this course.\n",
    score, grade);

    switch(grade)
    {
        case 'A':    printf("Great job!!\n");
                     break;
        case 'B':    printf("Well done!\n");
                     break;
        case 'C':    printf("Mission Accomplished.\n");
                     break;
        case 'D':    printf("Perhaps you need to consider repeating?\n");
                     break;
        default:     printf("See you next semester?\n");
    }
}
```

Why the need for the break statements?   Figure 5-21 from page 256:

Course Standard: Please note how the indentation is handled in a switch construct.

Why are the values being compared with the control expression in single quotes?

Without the break statement as soon as one one true case is found all following code will be executed!

```
Enter the score for the course: 94
Based on your score of 94, you will receive the grade of A in this course.
Great job!!
Well done!
Mission Accomplished.
Perhaps you need to consider repeating?
See you next semester?
```

Course Standard:

147

Switch Statement Rules

1.

2.

3.

4.

5.

6.

Example of Rule #4, the first statement is printed if value of grade 'A' or 'B'

```
switch(grade)
{
    case 'A':
    case 'B':    printf("Great job!!\n");
                 break;
    case 'C':    printf("Mission Accomplished.\n");
                 break;
    case 'D':    printf("Perhaps you need to consider repeating?\n");
    default:     printf("See you next semester?\n");
}
```

Revision of switch above using the ASCII values (how to compare integer data within a switch construct):

```
switch(grade)
{
    case 65:
    case 66:    printf("Great job!!\n");
                break;
    case 67:    printf("Mission Accomplished.\n");
                break;
    case 68:    printf("Perhaps you need to consider repeating?\n");
                break;
    default:    printf("See you next semester?\n");
}
```

Misuse of switch:	Improvement by reducing number of cases:	Alternative use of switch for range testing:
```switch(score)\n{\n case 100:\n case 99:\n case 98:\n case 97:\n case 96:\n case 95:\n case 94:\n case 93:\n case 92:\n case 91:\n case 90: grade = 'A'\n break;\n case 89:\n case 88:```	```switch(score / 10)\n{\n case 10:\n case 9: score = 'A';\n break;\n case 8: score = 'B';\n break;\n case 7: score = 'C';\n break;\n case 6: score = 'D';\n break;\n default: score = 'F';\n}```	```switch(score)\n{\n case 90 ... 100: grade = 'A';\n break;\n case 80 ... 89: grade = 'B';\n break;\n case 70 ... 79: grade = 'C';\n break;\n case 60 ... 69: grade = 'D';\n break;\n case 0 ... 59: grade = 'F';\n break;\n default: grade = '?';\n}```

Reminder:

- There is a temptation to only and always make use of the if...else with for all selection needs.

- Consider whether the use of a switch of conditional expression might be a better choice in some situations. The result may be shorter and more readable logic.

149

Chapter 6 - Repetition

The real power of computers is the ability to rapidly repeat an operation or series of operations. The act of such repetition is commonly referred to as **looping** but this term does not incorporate all techniques of repetition.

Looping Basics and Terminology

- If **figure 6-1 (page 304)** represents a loop on flow chart, then you are probably wondering when and how the looping stops.

First, a few terms:

- loop iteration -

- loop control expression -

- loop initialization -

- loop update -

- loop control variable -

Repetition Flowchart Example #1:

Write an algorithm to calculate the average, maximum, and minimum of an unknown number of exam values. The scores on the test can range from 0 – 100 and will all be integer values.

Repetition

- To complete this problem we need the ability to repeat a number of instructions.
- Repetition permits us to identify certain code to be repeated while a certain logical expression is true.

Step #1 – What is specified of the program?

- Input – Integers between 0 and 100, inclusive of the end points, until a value is entered to signify the end of input.
  - We **do not** need an array (subject of chapter 8) to store the entire data set in the memory of the computer. The memory necessary to solve this problem **will not** be dependent on the size of the data set (number of students taking the exam).
- Output – Average (floating-point), maximum (integer), and minimum values (integer).

Step #2 – Analyze the problem

- **What formulas are needed?** To calculate the average we need to know the sum of all scores and the number of scores. We will have to compare values as they are entered to determine their status as the maximum or minimum value.
- We also need to determine how the user will indicate that the input has ended.

How to approach the terminating input condition?

Structure Chart for Solution:

151

Step #3 – The Software Solution

- **Main function**

Why does this algorithm begin with initialization rather than input?

- First user-defined function (input task):

Second user-defined function (average variables updated)	**Third user-defined function (test for maximum score)**	**Fourth user-defined function (test for minimum score)**
Final user-defined function (output task)	The placement of the loop control expression divides looping constructs in to two categories, **pretest** and **post-test** loops. **Figure 6-2 page 305:**	
	Pretest Loop	**Post-test Loop**

153

In a **pretest** loop, the loop control expression must be true prior to iterating the loop even one time. Prior to the start of each consecutive iteration the loop control expression is re-evaluated and while that expression remains true the repetition continues. If the loop control expression is false then no further iterations will be conducted.

Key Point: The minimum number of times the body of a pretest loop will be iterated is **zero**. If the expression is never true, then the loop instructions (body of the loop) will **never be executed**.

In a **post-test** loop the instructions of the body of the loop will be executed prior to the evaluation of the loop control expression. The loop control expression will be evaluated at the end of each iteration to determine whether or not to continue.

- **What is the big difference?** The minimum number of times the body of a post-test loop will be iterated is one. Regardless if the expression is false the loop will iterate once and then test the condition to determine whether iteration continues. **Figure 6-4 (page 306):**

(a) Pretest Loop	(b) Post-test Loop

154

Example: Allow the user to enter a positive integer as input and calculate the product of all integers between 1 and the given input. This is calculating the **factorial** of the given input.

Factorial flow chart:

Identify the loop control variable:	Identify the type of loop:	Identify how the loop control variable is updated:	Is the algorithm logically correct when the user enters zero?

Event-Controlled and Counter-Controlled Loops

The factorial problem above is an example of a **counter-controlled loop**. The counter, which is also the loop control variable, controls the number of times the body of the loop is to be repeated.

In an **event-controlled loop**, an event takes place that changes the loop control expression from true to false and bringing the repetition to a halt. With such a process one can determine whether another iteration of the loop will take place but determining the number of remaining iterations is not possible.

- **Examples of event-controlled processes**:
  - Sum all of the non-negative numbers a user enters until that user enters a negative value as input.
  - **Explanation**: We cannot know how many numbers the user will enter! Perhaps during the first execution of the program the user just wants the sum of 14 numbers, but on the second execution of the program he desires to sum 31 numbers.
  - Accept input for the factorial problem above, but if the user enters a negative value print an error message to the screen and require the user to try the input process again.
  - **Explanation**: The event in both of the previous examples is user input where one particular input value does not inform you about the value (or the meaning) of the next input or the remaining number of data to be entered.

Key Point: If you can count or calculate the total number of iterations at will take place during the execution of a loop, then it is a **counter-controlled** process, otherwise the process is **event-controlled**.

Loops in C

The C programming language has three looping, or iterative, constructs: `while`, `for`, and `do-while`. We will look first at the syntax and applications of the `while` and `do-while` and come back to consider the same of the `for` loop.

The `while` Loop

The `while` construct is a **pretest** loop. As with all loops the `while` makes use of a control expression to determine whether the loop should continue to, or will ever, iterate. Being a **pretest** loop the loop control expression is evaluated prior to the first iteration of the loop, while the expression is evaluated to be true then the loop will complete another iteration.

- The iterations will continue WHILE the loop control expression is true. When the control expression evaluates to false the iterative process stops.

Basic Syntax of the While Loop

```
while (expression)
{
    //ONE OR MORE STATEMENTS TO REPEAT
    //BODY OF THE LOOP
}
```

Note: There is no semicolon after the loop control expression of the `while` statement, because the loop is followed a body which contains the actions to repeat.

Write a function that calculates n! for a given n.

```
int calcFactorial(int n)
{
    int nFact = 1;  //VALUE TO STORE N!

    while(n > 0)
    {
        nFact *= n;
        n = n - 1;
    }

    return(nFact);
}
```

Is there reason to be concerned that the value of zero is going to be multiplied?

The value entered by the user is stored locally in the variable n, how does changing n on each iteration influence what is going on back in the calling function?

The do-while Loop

The do-while construct is a **post-test** construct. Similar to the while a loop control expression is used to determine if repetition continues, but in the case of a post-test construct the expression is evaluated after the execution of the instructions inside of the body.

- In contrast to the while loop, the keyword while in a do-while is terminated with a semicolon.

Course Standard: Indent all statements that compose the body of a loop two spaces.

Course Standard: With all loops (and if statements) the braces that mark the start and end of the loop body MUST be used.

Basic Syntax of the Do While Loop

```
do
{

    //ONE OR MORE STATEMENTS TO REPEAT
    //BODY OF THE LOOP

}while(expression);
```

Note: As with the while loop, the do while loop will continue to iterate while the loop control expression evaluates true.

157

Input Validation

- The goal of **adding code to our input functions** is to ensure that before the function is allowed to terminate that we have a meaningful value to process in the remainder of our program.

  - The task of input validation is **commonly found within the input function**. Going forward from this point input functions will be more than print-scan-return statements making the use of such input functions apparent.

- You must always provide the user with an **unlimited number** of opportunities to enter meaningful data.

- Due to its complexity you **will not validate for particular data types** only for acceptable values within a specified data type.

  - You will assume that the user will always enter the expected data type as input.

- One important part of input validation is to display an **appropriate message** to the user making them aware of their mistake and that input which is desired.

- Because input validation does make input functions more complex it is **ill advised** to continue to use **pass by address** in an effort to "return" multiple values from a single input function. The syntax associated with pass by address and related pointer operations (chapters 9 and 10) make it easy to incorrectly apply such techniques to input validation.

Write a function to accept the input for a non-negative integer n for the purpose of calculating n!

```
int getN()
{
    int n;    //NUMBER TO BE INPUT BY USER

    do
    {
        printf("Enter value of n to calculate n!: ");
        scanf("%d", &n);

        if(n < 0)
        {
            printf("Error!  Please enter a non-negative value!\n\nn");
        }
    }while(n < 0);

    return(n);
}
```

- The user must be given an unlimited number of opportunities to enter correct data which necessitates the use of a loop. The program cannot proceed with processing the data before obtaining acceptable input from the user. A selection construct cannot guarantee an unlimited number of input opportunities to ensure valid data.

158

Why do we not use an "if loop" for input validation?

What is wrong with the term "if loop"?

Nested Loops

What is a nested loop?

How does that definition help solve problems that make use of nested loops?

What is the recommended approach to solving nested looping problems?

159

Example: Write a program that accepts two integer numbers a and b and print the factorial of each integer value in the range a to b.

- We have already confirmed that we are able to accept an integer and calculate the factorial of that number.

- Next we need to add to the existing program such that we can calculate each n! for all integers n in the range from a to b.

- New tasks or revisions needed:
  - Get the start and end values and validate both such that the end is not less than the start.
  - Calculate and print the factorial for each integer between start and end (inclusive).

```
int getStart();
int getEnding(int);
int calcFactorial(int);
void displayResults(int, int);
```

Why is there a parameter for getEnding **but none for** getStart?

```
int main()
{
    int nFact; //STORES n!
    int start;
    int end;

    start = getStart();
    end = getEnding(start);

    while(start <= end)
    {
        nFact = calcFactorial(start);
        displayResults(start, nFact);
        start++;
    }

    return(0);
}
```

Course Standard Note: A limited amount of control structures (selection, repetition) is permissible in the main function to ensure that it is the main function which makes most of the function calls for the program.

User-defined function for input of starting value:

```
int getStart()
{
    int n;

    do
    {
        printf("Enter starting integer value: ");
        scanf("%d", &n);

        if(n < 0)
        {
            printf("\n\nERROR!  Non-negative values only!!\n\n");
        }
    }while(n < 0);

    return(n);
}
```

User-defined function for input of ending value:

```
int getEnding(int start)
{
    int end;

    do
    {
        printf("Enter the ending value: ");
        scanf("%d", &end);

        if(end < start)
        {
            printf("\n\nERROR! Enter a value >= %d\n", start);
        }
    }while(end < start);

    return(end);
}
```

```
void displayResults(int n, int nFact)
{
    printf("%d! = %d\n", n, nFact);
}
```

- **Above, the output function.**

161

Where are the nested loops? It is common to first consider the examples below when one thinks of **nested** constructs.

Nested `while` **loop example:**	**Nested** `if` **construct example:**
| ```
while( )
{
   while( )
   {
   }
}
``` | ```
if( )
{
   if( )
   {
   }
}
``` |

Notes:

- In the nested loop example provided the loops are found in two different user-defined functions. One is in the `main` function that counts from the starting point to the ending point and the second is found in the function that calculates the factorial for each integer in the desired range.

- Every loop typically represents a task, or single process, in a program. If you can identify each of these individual tasks and factor them into individual user-defined functions you may find the complex problem easier to solve and test.

The Infinite Loop

This is not the next type of loop we need to introduce, there is no syntax for an infinite loop, such a loop can appear in many forms.

- An infinite loop is a **logical error**!
- You can terminate a program at any time by entering `CTRL-C` from the keyboard.

Example: Allow the user to enter integer values until a 1 or 2 is input.

Source:	**Output:**
| ```
do
{
   printf("Enter a value: ");
   scanf("%d", &userInput);

}while(userInput != 1 || userInput != 2);
``` | ```
Enter a value: 3
Enter a value: 2
Enter a value: 1
Enter a value:
``` |

- The control expression may seem logically correct, "accept input while the value entered is not 1 or 2", but logically it results in an infinite loop. There is no single value that cannot be **both** 1 and 2 at the same time.

162

In what forms can we observe an infinite loop?

Repetition Review - Three Common Loop Components

1. **Initialization** of loop control variable.
2. **Evaluation** of the loop control expression.
3. **Update** to the loop control variable.

The for loop

The for loop is a pretest (counter-controlled) loop that utilizes three expressions and places them all on a single line. These expressions (expr1, expr2, expr3) represent the three components previously listed.

Figure 6-12 (page 315) flowchart representation of a for loop:

When to use a for loop?

Expression 1 (Initialization)

- Expression 1 is evaluated only when the for loop is encountered for the first time. It is in this expression that the loop control variable will be initialized.

Expression 2 (Evaluation)

- After expression 1 is evaluated we immediately test expression 2 which is the loop control expression of the loop.
- If expression 2 is initially evaluated to be false then the loop will not iterate! The for loop is a pretest!
- Upon completion of every iteration the loop control expression must be re-evaluated to determine whether another iteration is needed.

Expression 3 (Update)

- This final expression is evaluated at the end of every iteration and before the re-evaluation of expression 2.
- Essentially, any expression changing the loop control variable is acceptable for the third expression.

Syntax

- Semicolons are necessary between expression 1 and 2 and between expression 2 and 3.
- As with any looping construct the for loop has a body and the body will begin and end with { and }. The body of instructions can be one or more instruction.

Comparison to the while loop (Figure 6-14, page 317):

What must be considered prior to attempting to make a conversion from a while loop to a for loop?

Without altering the initialization values, convert the `while` **loop into a for loop:**

```
int lcv = 1;
int n = 4;
int nFact = 1;

while(lcv <= n)
{
    nFact *= lcv;
    lcv++;
}
```

Converted loop:

Without altering the initialization values, convert the `while` **loop into a for loop:**

```
int lcv;
int n = 4;
int nFact = 1;

lcv = n;

while(lcv > 0)
{
    nFact *= lcv;
    lcv--;
}
```

Converted loop:

What potential concerns exist with the application of the `for` **loop below?**

```
int x;

for(x = -1; x < 0; )
{
    printf("Enter a non-negative integer: ");
    scanf("%d", &x);
}
```

Example: Right Triangle (page 327)

Given the number of rows as input write a program to print the following design (example shown is when the user wants the figure to have six total rows):

```
1
12
123
1234
12345
123456
```

Repetition Flowchart Example #2:

- Given a non-negative integer, re-arrange the digits of that integer to create the largest possible integer value.

Example Executions:

```
Enter an integer: 1230789
The sorted digit is 9873210

Enter an integer: 53635
The sorted digit is 65533
```

Step #1 – What is specified of the program?

- We expect an integer to be entered and to be output.
- Leading 0's do not make sense as input and will not be considered.
- All input will be non-negative and this must be validated.

Step #2 – Analyze the problem

- How do we extract a single digit from a number?
- How do we do this and then determine if it is the largest digit in the number?
- What do we do once we have the largest digit in the number?
- What about finding the second largest digit in the number?

More examples of the modulus operation:

- $53572 \% 10 =$

- $53572 \% 100 =$

- $53572 \% 1000 =$

- $53572 \% 10000 =$

Step #3 – Designing the Software Solution

What are the tasks of this program?

1. Get the input from the user.
2. Count the number of non-leading zero digits so we can append them to the value output at the end.
3. Find the largest digit in the input. "Add" it to a new number. "Delete" it from the value input.
4. Return to step #3 until ALL values, biggest to smallest, have been moved from the value input to the new integer value being constructed.
5. Append the zero digits on to the end of the new value.

`main` **Function**

ctzero **Function**

findMax **Function**

appendMax **Function**

removeMax **Function**

Solution:

```c
int getInput();
int ctZero(int);
int findMax(int, int*);
int appendMax(int, int);
int removeMax(int, int, int);
void output(int);

int main()
{
    int n;
    int sorted = 0;
    int max;
    int maxLoc;
    int zeroCount;

    n = getInput();

    zeroCount = ctZero(n);

    while(n > 0)
    {
        max = findMax(n, &maxLoc);
        sorted = appendMax(sorted, max);
        n = removeMax(n, max, maxLoc);
    }

    output(sorted * (int)pow(10, zeroCount));

    return(0);
}

int appendMax(int sorted, int max)
{
    return(sorted * 10 + max);
}

int removeMax(int n, int max, int maxLoc)
{
    return(n - max * (int)pow(10, maxLoc));
}
```

171

```c
int getInput()
{
    int n;

    do
    {
        printf("Enter an integer to sort: ");
        scanf("%d", &n);

        if(n < 0)
        {
            printf("\nError! Non-negative values only!\n\n");
        }
    }while(n < 0);

    return(n);
}

int ctZero(int n)
{
    int ct = 0;

    while(n > 0)
    {
        if(n % 10 == 0)
        {
            ct++;
        }

        n = n / 10;
    }

    return(ct);
}

void output(int sorted)
{
    printf("Sorted value: %d\n", sorted);
}
```

```c
int findMax(int n, int *maxLoc)
{
    int max = 0;
    int loc = 0;

    while(n > 0)
    {
        if(n % 10 > max)
        {
            max = n % 10;
            *maxLoc = loc;
        }

        n = n / 10;
        loc++;
    }

    return(max);
}
```

172

Review of Repetition Constructs and Techniques

	Pretest	Post-Test
Counter-Controlled		
Event-controlled		

Advanced Topic - Recursion

- **Recursion** is a repetitive process in which a function calls itself.
- The **factorial** is one of the most common first examples given to demonstrate the use of recursion.

Solving the factorial with the `while` loop:

```
int factorial(int n)
{
int nFact = 1;   //VALUE TO STORE N!
int lcv = 1;

while(lcv <= n)
{
nFact *= lcv;
lcv++;
}

return(nFact);

}
```

Solving the factorial using a recursive function:

```
int factorial(int n)
{
int nFact = 1;

if(n > 1)
{
nFact = n * factorial(n - 1);
}

return(nFact);

}
```

What is the recursive case for the factorial solution?

What is the base case for the factorial solution?

173

The following on recursion is adapted from: http://www.nist.gov/dads/HTML/recursion.html

Every recursive solution involves two cases, the second part having three components.

- **Base case(s)**, in which the problem is simple enough to be solved directly.
  - When the base case is reached there are no more recursive function calls and the function can begin the process of returning to previously called occurrences of the function.
- **Recursive case(s)**. A recursive case has three components:
  - divide the problem into one or more simpler or smaller (sub)parts of the same problem,
  - call the function (recursively) on each part, and
  - combine the solutions of the parts into a solution for the problem.

Depending on the problem, any of these may be trivial or complex.

Note: A function always returns control (and sometimes a value) to the function that called it. It does not matter if the functions have unique names or are the same as is the case in recursion.

Note: Calling a function is different than an iteration of a loop where the same code inside of the loop is being executed repeatedly. Each function call is independent of other function calls with local variables occupying unique memory locations.

Limitations of Recursion

- Expensive overhead due to the number of function calls.
- A large number of function calls will require a large amount of memory.

When should you NOT use recursion?

Chapter 7 - External Input/Output

When might there be too much data?

- ...a program that produces so much output it scrolls quickly off of the screen.
- ...a program that accepts too much data to be input by hand.
- ...you grow tired to testing your program with the same test data over and over and over...

Solution? Get the data from a file! Send the output to a file!

Redirection of Input and Output

- Redirection has nothing to do with any programming language. It is a tool of the operating system that will permit the input of data from a file and/or the output to a file.
- To use redirection (of either input or output) you must first have created an executable (a.out) file.
- If using redirection for input, you must create your data file.

Example: Write a program that will accept scores as input until the user enters a −1. After the −1 value has been entered, the input will stop and the user will be presented the average of all scores entered.

```
#define EXIT -1

int getInput();
float calcAverage(int, int);

int main()
{

    int count = 0;
    int sum = 0;
    int currentScore;

    do
    {

        currentScore = getInput();
        if(currentScore != EXIT)
        {

            sum += currentScore;
            count++;

        }

    }while(currentScore != EXIT);

    printf("The average of the entered scores is: %.2f\n", calcAverage(sum, count));

    return(0);

}
```

```
int getInput()
{
    int score;

    printf("Enter the score: ");
    scanf("%d", &score);

    return(score);
}

float calcAverage(int s, int c)
{
    return((float)s / c);
}
```

Why is it important to test your program with the same data sets as you correct logical errors?

Next Task: To create a data file that will contain the data for this program (all of the scores). We can place one value per line, with the last value being a –1 to terminate the input phase or we can place the data on a single line separated by spaces.

Example Data File #1 (assume the data file name is data):

1 3 2 –1

To accept the data from this file rather than from the keyboard, enter the following at the UNIX prompt: `a.out  <  data`

And the output would look a little something like this:

```
Enter the score: Enter the score: Enter the score: Enter the score: The average of the
entered scores is: 2.00
```

Notice that all of the input prompts are on the same line? Why does this happen?

Example Data File #2:

5 8 7 6 –1

Redirection can also be used to output to a file.

`a.out < data > output`

- With the above statement, both the input comes from and the output goes to an external file.

The contents of `output`:

```
Enter the score: Enter the score: Enter the score: Enter the score: Enter the score: The average of the
entered scores is: 6.50
```

What happens when we attempt to take data from another file and send the output to an existing file?

(for example `a.out < data2 > output`)

How can you redirect output to append to the end of an existing file?

Why is the redirection of output rarely used without also redirecting input?

In what order is data read from a file?

Note: Any type of white space (tab, new line, single space) can be used to separate data in a file.

Note #2: If your data file has an extension (such as `.dat` or `.txt`) then it must be referenced in the redirection command.

Note: The programming in this section will be covered in Octave, a program that is "mostly compatible" with MATLAB, and not in the C Programming language.

How to make use of Octave?

Can I still use MATLAB?

Important MATLAB/Octave Terminology:

- **File id -**

- **File handle -**

Making a Connection to a File

Before we can utilize external files for input or output we must successfully establish a connection with the file, or files, of interest. Two standard functions have been provided for our use to access an external file for input or output.

- `fopen` - opens a text file
- `fclose` - closes a text file

You use `fopen` to establish a connection to an external file. It opens the file for a specified mode (the three most common are `r`, `w`, and `a`, for read, write, and append) and we initialize the **file handle** by assigning it to the results returned from an `fopen` statement.

The `fopen` statement works as follows:

```
fh = fopen('filename', 'r');
```

- The external file name is the file to which we want to establish a connection.
- The second value is the mode in which we intend to use the file.

178

Table 7-1 page 400:

Mode	Meaning

Figure 7-4 (page 400) describes the open modes:

Opening a file, and testing for success:

```
fh = fopen('data', 'r');

if(fh ~= -1)
    fprintf('Open Success!\n');
else
    fprintf('Open Failed!\n');
end
```

If there is a file called data that we can open in the same directory as the current .m file then the value that is assigned to the file variable fh is non-negative.

- If the file cannot be opened a -1 value will be assigned to fh.

179

How, why, and when should we close a file handle?

- How - `fclose(file handle variable);`
- When - as soon as you are finished accessing the external file!
  - Do not attempt to close a file handle that failed to initialize in MATLAB/Octave (stores -1 value).

Course Standards Regarding File I/O:

- Always test to make sure a connection to the external file has been successfully established.
- Utilize `fclose` as previously described.

Input/Output from/to an External File (using file handle variables)

When our input/output has come from the standard streams (`stdin`, `stdout`) we used functions such as `printf` and `scanf` (`fprintf` and `input` in MATLAB/Octave). We will need alternative functions now that we expect our data to come from a source other than the standard input stream or output to be written to an alternative external destination.

- `fprintf` - prints formatted output to a file
- `fscanf` - reads formatted input from a file

Reading Data from a File

After we have a file opened for reading we need to read data from it. We know (in advance) that there are 10 integers in the external file to be read. Read those 10 values (seen below) from an external file named `data` and display the `sum` to the screen.

```
20 30 40 50 60 70 80 90 95 5

sum = 0;
fh = fopen('data', 'r');

if(fh ~= -1)

    for i = 1 : 10
        currentScore = fscanf(fh, '%d', 1);
        fprintf('i: %d value read: %d\n', i, currentScore);
        sum = sum + currentScore;
    end

    fclose(fh);

    fprintf('Sum of all scores is: %d\n', sum);

else
    fprintf('External file failed to open!\n');
end
```

180

The `fscanf` **works as follows:**

```
variable = fscanf(file handle, format string, size);
```

- The argument size in combination with the number of placeholders in the format string specifies the amount of data to be read from the file.

Concerning arrays in your MATLAB/Octave programs in CS 159:

Detecting the End of a File (of Unknown Length)

- The `feof` (where EOF represents End Of File) function will return 1 when the end of the file has been reached.
- We want to continue reading data while we have NOT reached the end of the file.

Example external data file:

```
20 30 40 50 60 70 80 90 95 85
75 65 55 45 35 25 15 5
```

Modification of program to work with an external file of unknown length:

```
sum = 0;
fh = fopen('data', 'r');

if(fh ~= -1)

    while(~feof(fh))
        currentScore = fscanf(fh, '%d', 1);
        fprintf('feof(fh) = %d value read: %d\n', feof(fh), currentScore);
        sum = sum + currentScore;
    end

    fclose(fh);

    fprintf('Sum of all scores is: %d\n', sum);
else
    fprintf('External file failed to open!\n');
end
```

- **Problem (with the program above)? OUTPUT IS WRONG!**

The previous program does not produce correct results. Counting the number of times the print statement inside of the loop is executed would result in one more than the number of integers in the external file. This informs us that the `feof` function does not return a true value indicating that the end of the file has been reached until after an attempt to read has failed because no more data is present in the file.

Correction: Do not process data that is not part of the set. Only add to the `sum` if we are **NOT** at the end of the file.

How to modify the previous code segment to intercept when the `fscanf` function is unable to read any new data (EOF reached):

Positioning in a File

Example: In a file called `dataGrade` are the student data for a given course. The data is in the form of student ID (`int`) followed by score (`float`) followed by grade (`char`). One or more spaces separate all data. Each row represents a single student. Open this file and determine the number of each grade in the course. **Note:** The data file DOES NOT contain any column heading text.

Source File (`dataGrade`)

```
1234    77.54    C
3444    93.22    A
3221    77.60    C
3244    66.50    D
9392    99.00    A
1112    95.00    A
3666    88.99    B
3299    55.40    F
5455    84.33    B
```

Output Desired

```
Grade report
A's - 3
B's - 2
C's - 2
D's - 1
F's - 1
```

Is all of the data in the external file necessary to generated the desired output?

Solution:

```
fIn = fopen('dataGrade', 'r');
aCt = 0;
bCt = 0;
cCt = 0;
dCt = 0;
fCt = 0;

if(fIn ~= -1)

    while(~feof(fIn))

        grade = fscanf(fIn, '%d %*f %c', 1);

        if(~feof(fIn))
            switch(grade)
                case 'A'   aCt = aCt + 1;
                case 'B'   bCt = bCt + 1;
                case 'C'   cCt = cCt + 1;
                case 'D'   dCt = dCt + 1;
                otherwise  fCt = fCt + 1;
            end
        end
    end

    fprintf('Grade Report\n');
    fprintf('A - %d\n', aCt);
    fprintf('B - %d\n', bCt);
    fprintf('C - %d\n', cCt);
    fprintf('D - %d\n', dCt);
    fprintf('F - %d\n', fCt);

    fclose(fIn);

else
    fprintf('Unable to open data file!\n');
end
```

Why the use of the * between the % and the conversion code?

Chapter 8 – Arrays

The data types we have studied so far have been simple, predefined types and variables of these types are used to represent a single value.

Problem: We want to accept input that represents student scores on a recent exam. We would like to calculate the maximum, minimum, average, median, and mode. We know from a previous example that we can calculate maximum, minimum, and average without needing to store all of the scores in variables (the memory of the computer), but to calculate the median and mode we do need to keep all values and sort those values to make these calculations.

What if we knew the number of students were 10? One possibility may include declaring variables for each value to be entered...

Declarations to store scores:

Figure 8-2 (page 460):

```
int score0;
int score1;
int score2;
int score3;
int score4;
int score5;
int score6;
int score7;
int score8;
int score9;
```

And to read and manipulate data (**Figure 8-3 page 461**):

Perhaps it is possible to manage this small number of variables, but what if I had 100 students? Or even 1,000 students?

- It is not practical to declare individual variables for each value.
- What is needed is a more practical way to store and access a collection of related data items.

An **array** is a **consecutive** series of **variables** that share one name and data type. Each variable (or **element**) that composes the array has a number known as an **index value** that represents its position in the array. When we reference the name of the array along with a given index value we are referring to a specific individual value stored in that array.

Arrays of scores (Figure 8-4 page 462):

Figure 8-7 (page 464) gives examples of declaring and defining arrays:

Declaring and Defining Arrays

- Declaration and definition inform the compiler of the **name** of the array, the **size** of the array, and the **data type** of each element.
- C provides for two different array types; fixed-length arrays (length is known before program is compiled) and variable-length arrays (size is determined when program is running).

Course Standard: All arrays will be **static** (of fixed-length) until we introduce the topic of **dynamic** memory allocation in chapters 9 and 10. The application of variable-length arrays as seen in the example on pages 478-479 **will violate course standards** as it permits the local declarations and executable statements in a function to overlap.

- **Note:** it will be a standard for the course to replace the number (size) between [and] with a **symbolic constant** for a majority of statically declared arrays.

Accessing Elements in Arrays

- C uses an **index** to access individual **elements** in an array.
- The index value must be an integral value including an expression that evaluates to an integral value.

Assignment of Values into an Array

Write a program that will assign the score of 100 to the first element in the array exams. Next, print that element to the screen.

```
#define NUMEXAMS 3

    int exams[NUMEXAMS];    //ARRAY TO HOLD EXAM SCORES

    exams[0] = 100;

    printf("First exam score: %d\n", exams[0]);
```

Input of Values into an Array

```
#define NUMEXAMS 3

    int exams[NUMEXAMS];    //ARRAY TO HOLD EXAM SCORES

    printf("Enter score for exam 1: ");
    scanf("%d", &exams[0]);

    printf("First exam score: %d\n", exams[0]);
```

Why the use of %d in the printf **and** scanf **seen above?**

It is more common to use a loop when handling I/O tasks related to multiple elements of an array (**figure 8-5 page 462**):

186

Example using a loop to access the elements of an array:

```
#define NUMLABS 12

int lcv;   //LOOP CONTROL VARIABLE TO ACCESS ELEMENTS OF labs
int labs[NUMLABS];   //ARRAY TO HOLD LAB SCORES

for(lcv = 0; lcv < NUMLABS; lcv++)
{
    printf("Enter score for lab %d: ", lcv + 1);
    scanf("%d", &labs[lcv]);
}

for(lcv = 0; lcv < NUMLABS; lcv++)
{
    printf("You entered a score of %d for lab #%d.\n", labs[lcv], lcv + 1);
}
```

Initialization of Arrays

- It is possible to initialize the values of an array at the time of declaration.

```
#define NUMPROJECTS 4

int projects[NUMPROJECTS] = {75, 70, 85, 88};   //PROJECTS ARRAY INITIALIZED
int lcv;   //LOOP CONTROL VARIABLE FOR ACCESSING ELEMENTS OF projects

for(lcv = 0; lcv < NUMPROJECTS; lcv++)
{
    printf("The score for project #%d: %d\n", lcv + 1, projects[lcv]);
}
```

What if we attempted the following initialization?

187

Example of initializing all elements of an array to zero:

```
#define NUMPROJECTS 4

int projects[NUMPROJECTS] = {0};   //PROJECTS ARRAY INITIALIZED
int lcv;   //LOOP CONTROL VARIABLE FOR ACCESSING ELEMENTS OF projects

for(lcv = 0; lcv < NUMPROJECTS; lcv++)
{
    printf("The score for project %d = %d\n", lcv + 1, projects[lcv]);
}
```

Index Range Checking

- What if we try to access an element of the array that is outside of the index range declared?

For example, what if we tried to access projects[42] when the only valid index values are 0 – 3 for an array declared to be of size 4?

- **Remember:** The valid range of index values for an array of a given SIZE is 0 to the SIZE – 1.
- **The compiler does not check the boundary of an array!** Theoretically, you can go on forever beyond the defined limit of the array. However, when going outside of the bounds we are invading memory that we did not request and might have been reserved for another variable (or program), or trying to access memory that does not even exist.

What are the possible consequences for attempting to access an index that is outside of the bounds of an array?

Possible Observation	Reason why this may occur?
No problem, program works as expected.	
Program executes, but results are unexpected.	
Program crashes.	

Arrays and Functions (Inter-Function Communication)

- To process arrays in a large program, you have to be able to pass them to functions.

You can do this one of two ways:

- Pass (some or all) individual elements that compose the array.
- Pass the entire array.

Within each method we must understand the following:

1. How the **function declaration**, **function call**, and **function definition** changes in terms of syntax.

2. Whether the values being passed are **by value** or **by address** and if a method other than the default can be used.

Passing Individual Elements

You can pass individual elements to a function like any other variable, as long as the array element type matches the function parameter type, it can be successfully passed to a function.

Figure 8-11 (page 474) demonstrates how passing an individual element of an array is similar to passing an individual variable of the same data type:

Could you tell from the declaration of this "fun" function whether the integer being sent to the function is a single element of an integer array?

How is the "fun" function definition different from previous functions we have seen this semester given that the variable x is receiving an integer value that is an element of an integer array?

Example: Given an initialized integer array, print the square of each integer in the array.

```
#define ARRAYSIZE 5

void print_square(int);

int main()
{
  int lcv;
  int base[ARRAYSIZE] = {3, 7, 2, 4, 5};

  for(lcv = 0; lcv < ARRAYSIZE; lcv++)
  {
    print_square(base[lcv]);
  }

  printf("\n");

  return(0);
}

void print_square(int x)
{
  printf("%d squared = %d\n", x, x * x);
}
```

Observation from the previous program:

- When passing a single element of an array to a function you must specify the name of the array followed by the specific index of the value being passed in between the [ ] braces.

Review of Pass By Value

- Recall if we pass a single variable to a function that it is only a copy of the variable's value that is sent to the function such that changes to this copy does not change the passed variable.

- How is a single element of an array passed to a function? The first example that follows demonstrates the pass by value technique as demonstrated in chapter 4. The second example attempts to demonstrate whether a single element of an array is passed by value or by address.

  - Should x[1] be 24 in the final print statement then we would conclude that the element was **passed by value**.

  - Should x[1] be 3 in the final print statement then we would conclude that the element was **passed by address**.

190

```
void passByValue(int);

int main()
{
    int x = 32;

    printf("The value of x is %d\n", x);
    passByValue(x);
    printf("The value of x is %d\n", x);

    return(0);
}

void passByValue(int g)
{
    printf("The value of g is %d\n", g);
    g = g / 8;
    printf("The value of g is %d\n", g);
}
```

Output of program above:

```
#define ARRAYSIZE 3

void passByValue(int);

int main()
{
    int x[ARRAYSIZE] = {16, 24, 32};

    printf("The value of x[1] is %d\n", x[1]);
    passByValue(x[1]);
    printf("The value of x[1] is %d\n", x[1]);

    return(0);
}

void passByValue(int g)
{
    printf("The value of g is %d\n", g);
    g = g / 8;
    printf("The value of g is %d\n", g);
}
```

Output of program above:

From the output you can see that a single element of an array is treated the same as a single variable being passed to a function, that is, a **single element of an array is passed by value.**

- Is it possible to make use of pass by address with individual elements of an array?

191

From **8-12 (page 475)** demonstrates how passing an individual element of an array by address is similar to passing an individual variable of the same data type by address:

Example: Swap two elements of an array by passing them both by address to a function.

```
#define SIZE 10

void swapValues(int*, int*);

int main()
{
    int x[SIZE] = {3, 4, 5, 1, 2, 9, 8, 7, 6, 0};

    printf("x[4] = %d x[5] = %d\n", x[4], x[5]);

    swapValues(&x[4], &x[5]);

    printf("x[4] = %d x[5] = %d\n", x[4], x[5]);

    return(0);
}

void swapValues(int *ax, int *ay)
{
    int temp;

    temp = *ax;
    *ax = *ay;
    *ay = temp;
}
```

Example: Passing the x[1] element by address.

```
#include<stdio.h>

#define ARRAYSIZE 3

void passByValue(int*);

int main()
{
    int x[ARRAYSIZE] = {16, 24, 32};

    printf("The value of x[1] is %d\n", x[1]);
    passByValue(&x[1]);
    printf("The value of x[1] is %d\n", x[1]);

    return(0);
}

void passByValue(int *g)
{
    printf("The value of g is %d\n", *g);
    *g = *g / 8;
    printf("The value of g is %d\n", *g);
}
```

Passing the Whole Array

- What if we have an array of size 10 and we need to pass all 10 elements to a function?

Option #1, Pass Every Element

```
void fun(int, int, int, int, int, int, int, int, int, int);
```

Option #2, Pass Entire Array

```
void fun(int[]);
```

Figure 8-13 (page 475):

When passing the whole array to a function you only need to list the name of the array.

DO NOT include any of the following:

Example: Calculate the average of the values in a 50-element integer array:

```c
#define ARRAYSIZE 50

float average(int[]);

int main()
{
    int lcv;
    int base[ARRAYSIZE];
    float avg;

    for(lcv = 0; lcv < ARRAYSIZE; lcv++)
    {
        scanf("%d", &base[lcv]);
    }

    avg = average(base);
    printf("The average = %.2f\n", avg);

    return(0);
}
```

```c
float average(int b[])
{
    int lcv;
    float avg = 0.0;

    for(lcv = 0; lcv < ARRAYSIZE; lcv++)
    {
        avg += b[lcv];
    }

    avg = avg / ARRAYSIZE;

    return(avg);
}
```

Next revision: Move the task of input to a user-defined function.

- But how do we return an array from a function? Do we really need to?

Passing the Whole Array

```c
float average(int[]);
void getData(int[]);

int main()
{
    int base[ARRAYSIZE];
    float avg;

    getData(base);

    avg = average(base);
    printf("The average = %.2f\n", avg);

    return(0);
}
```

Important Note:

- If the value of the array is changed by what happened in getData then we can rule out pass by value as being the method of passing whole arrays between functions.

194

```
void getData(int b[])
{
    int lcv;

    for(lcv = 0; lcv < ARRAYSIZE; lcv++)
    {
        scanf("%d", &b[lcv]);
    }
}
```

More Important Notes:

- Consider this; if arrays were passed by value then this requires a complete duplication of memory necessary to store the copy of the array. This would be a very inefficient use of memory.

- Rather than passing a copy of the array the language passes the address of the array.

- No & operator in the user-defined function call as in chapter 4? **The name of an array already references a memory address!**

What would be the result of the print statement below if it were inserted into the main function ?

```
printf("base = %d\n", base);
```

What does the name of an array represent?

What does an index value represent?

Why are index range violations possible?

195

Problems to Solve In Class:

1. The new house you just purchased has a row of 20 trees in the back yard and being the peculiar engineer that you are you want no tree to be taller than the one that comes before it. Given the height of the trees from first (closest to your house) to last (farthest from your house) calculate the new tree heights.

```
Enter 20 integer plant height values: 30 30 30 32 30 30 28 28 30 30 30 28 28 25 25 28 30 28 24 25
New plant height values: 30 30 30 30 28 28 28 28 28 28 28 25 25 25 25 24 24
```

2. Write a function that will reverse the elements of an array (of ARRAYSIZE) so that the first element becomes the last and the last becomes the first, and so on...

Less Efficient Algorithm

More Efficient Algorithm

In what ways is the more efficient algorithm an improvement over the less efficient approach?

197

Sorting Introduction

Often data requires to be sorted in order to be processed further. This is evident when one considers data such as medical records, student academic records, or banking records. Without sorting data by some common field (last name or identification numbers) it would be difficult to locate and access a desired record when the number of patients, students, or bank customers becomes large.

Before we begin to look at the following simple sorting algorithms accept this disclaimer:

- *The simplest algorithms perform poorly. We introduce them to you as beginners because they are relatively easy to understand, write, test, and debug. Much more complex algorithms are often needed for good performance; such algorithms require data structures too complex for this course.*

There are a few important terms we need to clarify prior to explaining the sorting algorithms we will study this semester.

- **List** - In the first three sorting algorithms below we will divide an array into two lists, one list will be the **sorted list** and the other will be the **unsorted list**. The goal being to grow the sorted list and shrink the unsorted list until every element of the array is in the sorted list.
- **Pass** - Each of the algorithms below will move one element from the unsorted list to the sorted list. As previously mentioned this will continue until all items are a part of the sorted list. The process of moving one item from the unsorted list to the sorted list is known as a **pass**. [The final pass through the selection and bubble sorts will deviate from this general rule.]

Exchanging Values

- Sorting may require values found to be out of order (or unsorted) to be exchanged, or swapped.

For example, exchange the two elements found at index 1 and index 3 (**see Figure 8-9 and 8-10 on page 468**).

Correct Method of Exchanging Elements in an Array:

Incorrect Method of Exchanging Elements in an Array:

198

Selection Sort (page 491)

- Description of algorithm:

Bubble Sort (page 494)

- **Description of algorithm:**

200

Insertion Sort (page 497)

- **Description of algorithm:**

201

The Bubble Sort

The only sorting algorithm we will worry about coding is the Bubble Sort. The code is different from the code given in the book.

```c
#define NUMDATA 10

void bubbleSort(int[]);
void getData(int[]);
void printData(int[]);

int main()
{
    int data[NUMDATA]; //ARRAY TO HOLD DATA TO SORT

    getData(data);
    printData(data);    //PRINT BEFORE STATE
    bubbleSort(data);
    printData(data);    //PRINT AFTER STATE

    return(0);
}

void printData(int x[])
{
    int lcv;  //LOOP CONTROL VARIABLE TO ACCESS ARRAY

    for(lcv = 0; lcv < NUMDATA; lcv++)
    {
        printf("x[%d] = %d\n", lcv, x[lcv]);
    }
}

void getData(int x[])
{
    int lcv;  //LOOP CONTROL VARIABLE TO GET DATA

    for(lcv = 0; lcv < NUMDATA; lcv++)
    {
        scanf("%d", &x[lcv]);
    }
}
```

202

```
void bubbleSort(int x[])
{
    int numPasses;  //LCV THAT CONTROLS # OF PASSES
    int lcv; //LOOP CONTROL VARIABLE FOR SORTING
    int temp;  //HOLDS VALUE DURING SWAP

    for(numPasses = 1; numPasses < NUMDATA; numPasses++)
    {
        for(lcv = 0; lcv < NUMDATA - numPasses; lcv++)
        {
            if(x[lcv] > x[lcv + 1])
            {
                temp = x[lcv];
                x[lcv] = x[lcv + 1];
                x[lcv + 1] = temp;
            }//END OF IF
        }//END OF NEIGHBOR COMPARING LOOP
    }//END OF PASSES LOOP
}//END OF FUNCTION
```

Modify the Bubble Sort to work with an array that may not contain NUMDATA elements:

```
void bubbleSort(int x[], int size)
{
    int numPasses;  //LCV THAT CONTROLS # OF PASSES
    int lcv;        //LOOP CONTROL VARIABLE FOR SORTING
    int temp;       //HOLDS VALUE DURING SWAP

    for(numPasses = 1; numPasses < size; numPasses++)
    {
        for(lcv = 0; lcv < size - numPasses; lcv++)
        {
            if(x[lcv] > x[lcv + 1])
            {
                temp = x[lcv];
                x[lcv] = x[lcv + 1];
                x[lcv + 1] = temp;
            }//END OF IF
        }//END OF NEIGHBOR COMPARING LOOP
    }//END OF PASSES LOOP
}//END OF FUNCTION
```

- How do you modify the bubble sort above so that the array is sorted from largest to smallest?

How many passes are required to guarantee an array of N elements is sorted?

Why is it possible for an array to reach a sorted state prior to the required number of passes to guarantee sorting?

How many elements are in the sorted listed of a 6 (six) element array for each of the algorithms below?

Pass Number	Selection / Bubble	Insertion
1		
2		
3		
4		
5		

Searching

Searching is the process used to find the location of a target among a list of objects. In the case of an array, searching means that given a value, we want to find the location (index value) of the value in the array.

- The **sequential search** will work with data that is not ordered. We also know in these examples that the data is unique.

Searching to find a known target in an array:

Searching when the target is not found in the array:

Searching Program #1 - Ask the user to enter a target value and return the location of that value in the array.

- If the value does not exist, please inform the user.

```
#define ARRAYSIZE 10
#define NOTFOUNDERROR -1

int searchArray(int[], int);
int getTarget();

int main()
{
    int array[ARRAYSIZE] = {3, 2, 1, 4, 5, 6, 9, 8, 10, 7}; //ARRAY TO SEARCH
    int target;  //VALUE USER WISHES TO FIND
    int index;   //INDEX OF USER'S VALUE IN ABOVE ARRAY

    target = getTarget();
    index = searchArray(array, target);

    if(index == NOTFOUNDERROR)
    {
        printf("The value %d does not exist in the array!\n", target);
    }
    else
    {
        printf("The value %d was found at index %d of the array.\n", target, index);
    }

    return(0);
}
```

Why make use of the value -1 to determine that the target value was not found in the array?

206

```c
int searchArray(int x[], int n)
{
    int lcv;  //LOOP CONTROL VARIABLE USED TO ACCESS ALL ARRAY ELEMENTS
    int index = NOTFOUNDERROR;

    for(lcv = 0; lcv < ARRAYSIZE; lcv++)
    {
        if(x[lcv] == n)
        {
            index = lcv;
            lcv = ARRAYSIZE;
        }
    }

    return(index);
}
```

The user-defined searching function above will search every element of the array until one of the following events takes place:

- The target is found, the loop terminates, and the index value is returned.
- The end of the array is reached, the loop terminates, and the "not found" value is returned.

```c
int getTarget()
{
    int target;

    do
    {
        printf("Please enter the target value: ");
        scanf("%d", &target);

        if(target < 0)
        {
            printf("Please enter a valid target value >= 0!\n");
        }
    }while(target < 0);

    return(target);
}
```

This type of search is known as the **sequential search** because each element of the array may potentially be referenced in order to find the desired element or to determine that element does not exist.

What is the goodness of the **sequential searching** algorithm?

- It works! It is simple.

What problems are associated with the use of the sequential searching algorithm?

What if we had a very large data set and the value we are looking for does not exist?	
What if multiple instances of the target value are potentially present in the array?	

The Binary Search

- It is possible to reduce the time (both average and worst-case) it takes to complete a search by using an alternative searching algorithm known as the **binary search**.
- The binary search does require that the **data in the array be sorted**.

Is there a cost associated with sorting data?	
Should the binary search always be used when searching?	

Assume we have the array given below, notice it is sorted and will remain sorted throughout the entire algorithm. A searching algorithm should never alter the data it searches!

What is the goodness of the **binary** search as applied to the example above?

- Only three comparisons were needed to find target (in the above example). A sequential search would have required 7.
- With each comparison made between the target and the element at the mid-point we eliminate approximately half (hence the name binary) of the remaining index values as a possible location where the target could be found.

209

How does the binary search compare with the sequential search when it comes to finding a value that doesn't exist?

- The **sequential search** requires EVERY element of the array to be searched to be sure that the value does not exist.

Let's see in the example below how the binary search deals with a value that does not exist!

210

Searching Program #2 - Ask the user to enter a target value and return the location of that value in the array.

- If the value does not exist, please inform the user.

```c
#define NOTFOUNDERROR -1
#define ARRAYSIZE 10

int binarySearch(int[], int);
int getTarget();

int main()
{
    int array[ARRAYSIZE] = {12, 13, 14, 15, 16, 21, 23, 24, 25, 33}; //ARRAY TO SEARCH
    int target; //VALUE WE ARE SEEKING
    int index;  //INDEX VALUE AT WHICH TARGET IS FOUND

    target = getTarget();
    index = binarySearch(array, target);

    if(index == NOTFOUNDERROR)
    {
        printf("Your value %d is not in the array\n", target);
    }
    else
    {
        printf("Your value %d is located at index %d.\n", target, index);
    }

    return(0);
}
```

```c
int getTarget()
{
    int target;
    do
    {
        printf("Please enter the target value: ");
        scanf("%d", &target);
        if(target < 0)
        {
            printf("Please enter a valid target value >= 0!\n");
        }
    }while(target < 0);

    return(target);
}

int binarySearch(int x[], int n)
{
    int first = 0;               //SMALLEST INDEX VALUE WE ARE CONSIDERING
    int last = ARRAYSIZE - 1;    //LARGEST INDEX VALUE WE ARE CONSIDERING
    int mid;                     //MID POINT INDEX THAT WE ARE CONSIDERING
    int index = NOTFOUNDERROR;

    do
    {
        mid = (first + last) / 2;
        if(n > x[mid])                          //TARGET GREATER THAN VALUE AT MID -> UPDATE FIRST
        {
            first = mid + 1;
        }
        else if(n < x[mid])                     //TARGET LESS THAN VALUE AT MID -> UPDATE LAST
        {
            last = mid - 1;
        }
        else                                    //TARGET HAS BEEN LOCATED IN THE ARRAY
        {
            index = mid;
            last = first - 1;                   //WHAT DOES THIS DO?  WOULD first = last + 1 ALSO WORK?
        }
    }while(first <= last);

    return(index);
}
```

212

The user-defined searching function will search the array until the `first` is greater than the `last` which would occur for one of the following reasons:

- The target is found.
- There are no elements in the array remaining as candidates to be searched.

Searching Data that is not Unique

- In this case we are trying to count the total number of occurrences of the target in the array rather than the locations of each target value.

- The binary search can be used to find a single occurrence of the target and then from that point look at the adjacent values to count any additional occurrence of the target in the array.

```c
#define NOTFOUNDERROR 0
#define ARRAYSIZE 10

int binarySearch(int[], int);
int getTarget();
int completeCounts(int[], int, int, int);

int main()
{
    int array[ARRAYSIZE] = {12, 15, 15, 15, 16, 21, 23, 24, 33, 33}; //ARRAY TO SEARCH
    int target; //VALUE WE ARE SEEKING
    int ct;  //INDEX VALUE AT WHICH TARGET IS FOUND

    target = getTarget();
    ct = binarySearch(array, target);

    if(ct == NOTFOUNDERROR)
    {
        printf("Your value %d is not in the array\n.", target);
    }
    else
    {
        printf("Total number of occurrences: %d.\n", ct);
    }

    return(0);
}
```

213

```c
int binarySearch(int x[], int n)
{
    int first = 0;
    int last = ARRAYSIZE - 1;
    int mid;
    int ct = NOTFOUNDERROR;
    do
    {
        mid = (first + last) / 2;
        if(n > x[mid])
        {
            first = mid + 1;
        }
        else if(n < x[mid])
        {
            last = mid - 1;
        }
        else
        {
            last = first - 1;
            ct = 1;
        }
    }while(first <= last);

    if(ct == 1)  //IF ONE IS FOUND, SEARCH ADJACENT INDEXES
    {
        ct += completeCounts(x, n, mid + 1, 1);
        ct += completeCounts(x, n, mid - 1, -1);
    }
    return(ct);
}

int completeCounts(int x[], int target, int start, int change)
{
    int ct = 0;

    while(start >= 0 && start < ARRAYSIZE && x[start] == target)
    {
        start += change;
        ct++;
    }
    return(ct);
}
```

214

Multidimensional Arrays

The arrays we have seen so far are **single dimension** arrays. Each single dimension array is nothing more than a single row of indexed column values.

With **multidimensional arrays** we can add a second dimension (multiple rows with numerous columns), a third dimension (planes, rows, and columns), and further as necessary. Your only limitation may be memory!

Figure 8-34 (page 510) Two-dimensional array:

- Each intersection of a row and column can hold a single value of the data type of the array.

Declaration and Defining Multidimensional Arrays

Multidimensional arrays, like single dimension arrays, must be declared and defined before being used. Declaration and definition tell the compiler the **name**, **data type**, and **size of each dimension** of the array.

Data Type	Identifier	Dimension Extents
int	dataPoints	[3] [5] [4];

How is the total number of elements in a multidimensional array calculated?

215

Figure 8-40 (page 520) A Three-dimensional Array:

A four-dimensional array:

Problem, calculate the average of each row in a two-dimensional array (similar to **Figure 8-38 on page 518**):

```c
#define ROWS 5
#define COLS 4

void printTable(int[][COLS], float[]);
void calcAvgs(int[][COLS], float[]);

int main()
{
   int table[ROWS][COLS] =
   {
     {1,  2,  3,  4},
     {2,  3,  4,  5},
     {3,  4,  5,  6},
     {4,  5,  6,  7},
     {5,  6,  7,  8}
   };
   float avgs[ROWS];

   calcAvgs(table, avgs);
   printTable(table, avgs);

   return(0);

}
```

```
void calcAvgs(int t[][COLS], float avgs[])
{
    int i;
    int j;
    int sum;

    for(i = 0; i < ROWS; i++)
    {
        sum = 0;
        for(j = 0; j < COLS; j++)
        {
            sum += t[i][j];
        }
        avgs[i] = (float) sum / COLS;
    }
}

void printTable(int t[][COLS], float avgs[])
{
    int i;
    int j;

    for(i = 0; i < ROWS; i++)
    {
        printf("Row #%d: ", i + 1);
        for(j = 0; j < COLS; j++)
        {
            printf("%d ", t[i][j]);
        }
        printf("Average: %.2f\n", avgs[i]);
    }
}
```

Why is it required to specify the extent of the second dimension in the function definition as seen above?

217

Chapter 11 - Strings - Character Arrays

- A **string** is a series (character array) of characters with the capability to be treated as a single unit.

In C we have variable-length strings, just as with other arrays, we can declare a string to be of any size. Hopefully, when we make the declaration that it is large enough to hold the necessary data and as with any array we don't want to exceed the bounds reserved (and minimize the amount of reserved memory left unused).

Similar to the numeric arrays we've already seen this semester, the compiler doesn't prevent us from exceeding the limits of an array. However, we can tell where the data in a string ends thanks to a character known as a delimiter. This delimiter character ' \0 ' represents the end of the data within a single character array. This will be important to many functions that operate with strings.

- **Why do we need a character to mark the end of the array?** There may come a time when the meaningful characters that compose a string do not fill the array, then how are we able to differentiate between meaningful and garbage character data? If all strings ALWAYS filled the array, then we would not need a character to act as a delimiter.

- **What is "variable" about the length of string?** The amount of the space reserved for the array that is actually used at any given time or during any given execution of the program.

Declaring Strings and Accessing String Elements

- A string is declared as a character array. We are able to access each individual element of such an array (a character).

Examining the elements of a character array:

```
int lcv;
char str[11] = "Good Day";

for (lcv = 0; lcv < 11; lcv++)
{
    printf("str[%2d] = %3c %5d\n", lcv, str[lcv], str[lcv]);
}

printf("\n");
```

Output:

```
str[ 0] =  G      71
str[ 1] =  o     111
str[ 2] =  o     111
str[ 3] =  d     100
str[ 4] =         32
str[ 5] =  D      68
str[ 6] =  a      97
str[ 7] =  y     121
str[ 8] =         0
str[ 9] =         0
str[10] =         0
```

- Where is the delimiter? Is it there?

Answer to previous question:

- Yes, the first 9 (of 11) positions of this array are filled with the string value and its delimiter.
- The initialization statement will add the delimiter to the end of the character array.

What is in the remaining **unused elements** (at index 9 and 10) of the character array?

- According to Figure 11-6 on page 669 of your text it appears that these values are unknown (garbage).
- However, because we initialized the array above the remaining elements are of value 0 (ASCII value of the delimiter).

218

String Input/Output Functions

Here is a point to ponder, if we want to load data into an array must we always input that data one element at a time until the array is filled? Would this imply that we have to enter one character at a time in order to fill a string?

- Good news! The answer is no! While we do not have a string data type available we do have many functions and features in C that allows us to operate with strings with some ease.

The %s Placeholder

- The `%s` placeholder represents a string and is used in both input and output functions.

Example of `%s` placeholder in action:

```
char str1[SIZE];

printf("Enter a string: ");
scanf("%s", str1);  //NOTICE NO &, WHY IS THIS?!

printf("The string you entered was %s.\n", str1);
```

Output:

```
Enter a string: Purdue
The string you entered was Purdue.
```

- The `scanf` function only reads in the data up until a new line ('\n') or any white space is entered.

```
Enter a string: Go Purdue
The string you entered was _____.
```

The solution? Find an alternative to `scanf`!

```
printf("Enter a string: ");
gets(str1);

printf("The string you entered was %s.\n", str1);
```

What happens to the '\n' character entered by the user? The `gets` function will accept the input, terminated by a new line, and make a delimiter-terminated string out of it. **See Figure 11-11 on page 682.**

219

Concerns with both `scanf` **and** `gets` **functions:**

- The compiler we are using this semester no longer remains silent regarding the potential problems associated with the `gets` function. `warning: the 'gets' function is dangerous and should not be used.`

What makes `gets` **(and for the same reason** `scanf`**) "dangerous" and "should not be used"?**

Alternative (safer) approach to input:

```
void getString(char x[])
{

    int index = 0;

    printf("Enter your string now: ");

    do
    {

        x[index++] = getchar();
    }while(index < SIZE && x[index - 1] != '\n');

    //REPLACE THE '\n' WITH A DELIMITER CHARACTER
    x[index - 1] = 0;

}
```

- The `getchar` function will accept the input of a single character.
- The `do-while` above will terminate the accepting of input when the user enters a new line character or when the defined size of the array has been reached.
- Because the `getchar` function handles only individual character input it does not place the delimiter character in the array, but it will place the new line character (ASCII value 10) into the array, the delimiter must be assigned to the array and will overwrite the new line character in the function above.

220

String Manipulation Functions

C provides us with a rich set of string functions that can be found in the `string.h` library. We will discuss a few of the functions here and more can be found in Appendix F of the text.

- Functions we will consider: `strcpy, strcmp, strlen, strstr` (revisit this function in chapters 9 and 10)

Copying Strings, it is easy to make a copy of an integer or double variable, but how about strings (applies to all arrays)? Can we use the assignment operator?

```
char str1[SIZE];
char str2[SIZE];

getString(str1);    //SEE USER-DEFINED FUNCTION ON PREVIOUS PAGE.

str2 = str1;

printf("The string you entered was %s.\n", str1);
printf("The copy of the string you entered is %s.\n", str2);
```

What is the message generated by the compiler?

- `error: incompatible types when assigning to type 'char[150]' from type 'char *'`

What is REALLY being assigned in the expression `str2 = str1` found in the example above?

- Recall that the name of an array represents a memory location. The address itself is the starting address of the memory allocated for the array. The assignment here attempts to have `str2` refer to the same memory as `str1`.

Why does the compiler not approve of this particular assignment expression?

- The memory allocated to a statically declared array is fixed in terms of size and location.

- Based on the previous statement we would say the memory address to which an array refers is **constant**.

221

Code to copy one string to another (iterative solution):

```
char str1[SIZE];
char str2[SIZE];
int lcv = 0;

getString(str1);    //FUNCTION DEFINITION IN AN EARLIER EXAMPLE

for(lcv = 0; lcv < SIZE; lcv++)
{
    str2[lcv] = str1[lcv];
}

printf("The value of lcv is %d\n", lcv);

printf("The string you entered was %s.\n", str1);
printf("The copy of the string you entered is %s.\n", str2);
```

Problem: How to modify the code above such that the copying stops when the delimiter character is found? We really are not particularly interested in making sure the data in the unused portion of the two arrays is equivalent.

```
char str1[SIZE];
char str2[SIZE];
int lcv;

getString(str1);    //FUNCTION DEFINITION IN AN EARLIER EXAMPLE

lcv = 0;

do
{
    str2[lcv] = str1[lcv];
}while(str2[lcv++] != '\0');

printf("The string you entered was %s.\n", str1);
printf("The copy of the string you entered is %s.\n", str2);
```

222

Alternative - using the `string.h` function `strcpy`

• The function `strcpy` will take the **second** argument and copy its value to the **first**. In this case, the contents of `str1` are copied to `str2`.

```
char str1[SIZE];
char str2[SIZE];

getString(str1);   //FUNCTION DEFINITION IN AN EARLIER EXAMPLE

strcpy(str2, str1);

printf("The string you entered was %s.\n", str1);
printf("The copy of the string you entered is %s.\n", str2);
```

Output:

```
Enter a string: program
The string you entered was program.
The copy of the string you entered is program.
```

String Copy (strcpy) example (Figure 11-14 page 693, Copying Strings):

Is there a concern with more data being copied than there were spaces reserved in memory?

223

Determining the Length of a String

Iterative Solution:

```
char str1[SIZE];
int lcv = 0;

getString(str1);   //FUNCTION DEFINITION IN AN EARLIER EXAMPLE

while(str1[lcv] != '\0')
{
    lcv++;
}

printf("The number of characters in the string: %d\n", lcv);
```

The second function from string.h to introduce is the strlen function which will return the number of characters in the string. This function does not count the terminal delimiter character.

Examples:

```
Enter a string: smart
The strlen of the string smart is 5
```

```
Enter a string: Purdue
The strlen of the string Purdue is 6
```

The strlen function returns an integer.

```
printf("The strlen of the string %s is %d\n", str1, (int) strlen(str1));
```

Comparing Two Strings

• Just as we cannot assign one string to another, neither can we test two strings for equality using ==, <, <=, >, >= .

Example:

```
char str1[SIZE];
char str2[SIZE];

getString(str1);   //FUNCTION DEFINITION IN AN EARLIER EXAMPLE

strcpy(str2, str1);

if(str1 == str2)
{
    printf("The strings are equal!\n");
}
```

One would assume if the relational operators compare contents of strings that ANY value entered would lead to the equal statement being printed every time the previous code segment is expected.

What is output and what does that tell us about what is being compared when using relational or equality operators with two strings?

Using `strcmp`, an example:

```
Enter a string: ABC123
Enter a string: ABC123
The strings are equal!

Enter a string: ABC123
Enter a string: ACC123
Negative.

Enter a string: ACC123
Enter a string: ABC123
Positive.
```

```
Enter a string: ABCD
Enter a string: ABC
Positive.

Enter a string: ABC
Enter a string: ABCD
Negative.

Enter a string: WXYZ
Enter a string: abcdef
Negative.
```

What about comparing `ABC123` with `ACB123`?

Above you can see the output of tests using the `strcmp` function.

- if the value of `strcmp` is 0, then the strings are equal.
- if the value of `strcmp` is negative, then the first string comes before the second string (based on ASCII values).
- if the value of `strcmp` is positive, then the second string comes before the first string (based on ASCII values).

What does the last (`WXYZ`, `abcdef`) output tell you about upper and lower case characters on the ASCII table?

- The upper-case alpha characters are at a lower ASCII value than those in the lower-case.

225

The code:

```
char str1[SIZE];
char str2[SIZE];
int cmp;

getString(str1);    //FUNCTION DEFINITION IN AN EARLIER EXAMPLE
getString(str2);    //FUNCTION DEFINITION IN AN EARLIER EXAMPLE

cmp = strcmp(str1, str2);

if(cmp == 0)
{
    printf("The strings are equal!\n");
}
else if(cmp < 0)
{
    printf("Negative.\n");
}
else
{
    printf("Positive.\n");
}
```

String Compare (strcmp) examples (Figure 11-17 page 698):

226

Problem to solve in class... Implement the ROT13 encryption algorithm.

227

Chapters 9 and 10 – Pointers and Pointer Applications

- A **pointer** is a variable that represents, or stores, another memory address (typically of another variable) and through the memory address the data stored there can be accessed.

Working With Addresses, the & Operator

We have seen the address operator (&) required in `scanf` statements and being used to pass variables by address to functions, but what does this operator really do?

- The address operator (&) will return the memory address (location) of a variable. In the table below you can see two character variables a and b. Both of these variables are given a unique location in the memory of the computer to store a character value. The `printf` statement will display the memory address of a and b and does not print the contents of these variables.
- The `%p` placeholder is commonly used to print the address of a variable. The `p` represents a pointer value (memory address).
  - It is not necessary to place the & before the name of an array as the name of an array already represents a memory address.

```
char a = 'X';
char b = 'y';

printf("Address of a = %p\n", &a);
printf("Address of b = %p\n", &b);
```

Address of a =
Address of b =

When we use the `scanf` function we need to send the address (or addresses) to which values input are to be stored.

- You may recall in chapter 4 that we did not place an address operator (&) before the name of a pointer variable when using `scanf`, this is due to the fact that pointer variables already represent a memory address.

Pointer Variables

- As with all variables we must declare a pointer before we can assign a memory address to it.
- The declaration of a pointer is quite similar to declaring a single variable, we need a data type and the name (identifier) of the variable with a * preceding the name to indicate that the variable is a pointer.

Sample Pointer Declarations:

- `int *x;`
- `float *y;`
- `char *z;`

Figure 9-10 from page 564:

When passing by address the pointers were initialized as a result of the address that was passed from the calling function:

- `void getInput(int *operand1, int *operand2)`

228

Where do the variables, as previously declared, x, y, and z initially point?

- **Answer:** We do not know! We have seen how this can be bad with variables already this semester; however, with pointers the garbage value may be an invalid memory address, then if the pointer is referenced before it is ever initialized the result will be a **segmentation fault**.

Where do the variables from the example getInput user-defined function declaration operand1 and operand2 initially point?

- **Answer:** The memory addresses of the parameters sent by the call to the getInput function.

Initialization of Pointers

In order for a pointer to be initialized we must provide a meaningful place in memory for it to point (reference). Another variable is one place to which a pointer can point. We need to **assign** (=) a memory address to the pointer.

Figure 9-12 from page 566:

```
int a = -123;
int *p;

p = &a; //p POINTS TO a

printf("The memory address of a is: %p\n", &a);
printf("The pointer p points to: %p\n", p);
```

Output:

Figure 9-6 from page 561:

229

Now that we have established a relationship between the pointer and the pointee what can be accomplished through the pointer?

- Pointing to (referencing) a memory address is useless if we cannot access (de-reference) the value stored at that memory address.

The printing the value of p in the previous code produces the address to which p points (references) and next we need a way to access (de-reference) the value stored in that memory location. The **indirection operator (*)** placed before the pointer variable will permit access (de-reference) to the value stored at the location to which the pointer references.

```
int a = -123;
int *p;

p = &a; //p POINTS TO a

printf("The value of a is: %d\n", a);
printf("The value to which p references is: %d\n", *p);
```

```
The value of a is: -123
The value to which p references is: -123
```

Example (Similar to figure 9-8, page 563 in text):

```
int a = 3;
int b;
int *x;
int *y;

x = &a;
y = x;
printf("*x = %3d  *y = %3d\n", *x, *y);

*x = 1;
printf("*x = %3d  *y = %3d  a = %3d\n", *x, *y, a);

a = 5;
printf("*x = %3d  *y = %3d  a = %3d\n", *x, *y, a);

x = &b;  //IS THIS A PROBLEM?  b WAS NEVER INITIALIZED!
printf("*x = %3d  *y = %3d  a = %3d  b = %3d\n", *x, *y, a, b);

*x = a * *y;
printf("*x = %3d  *y = %3d  a = %3d  b = %3d\n", *x, *y, a, b);
```

Output:

230

Arrays and Pointers

You might have already been able to make this observation, but arrays and pointers are related. The name of an array, much like that of a pointer, represents a memory address with the index representing the offset from that base address. Unlike a pointer, the address to which an array refers cannot change. (Recall the string copy example from chapter 11)

- **Key Point:** Pointer variables are variable (they can change the memory to which they point). Arrays will always point to the same memory and are constants in that respect. You will never find the name of an array (unless de-referenced or being used in combination with an index value) on the left side of an assignment statement.

Figure 10-1 (page 612):

- The address of a and the address of a[0] are one and the same.

Example, pass the whole array (which is by address) to a function and represent the array locally as a pointer.

```
#define SIZE 5

void printArray(int*);

int main()
{
    int x[SIZE] = {3, 5, 7, 9, 10};

    printArray(x);

    return(0);
}

void printArray(int *y)
{
    int lcv;

    for(lcv = 0; lcv < SIZE; lcv++)
    {
        printf("y[%d] = %d\n", lcv, y[lcv]);
    }
}
```

- Note on the example above: It is possible to utilize the pointer y above as if it were an array.

231

Pointer Arithmetic and Arrays (Section 10.2 - Single Dimension Arrays only)

- Using pointer arithmetic is an alternative method of accessing the elements of an array.

```
int main()
{
    int a[5] = {2, 4, 6, 8, 22};
    int i;

    for(i = 0; i < 5; i++)
    {
        printf("a[%d] = %d\n", i, *(a + i));
    }

    return(0);
}
```

Figure 10-7 (page 616):

As with index values, the value added to x represent an offset from the memory address value that x represents. The addition results in a new memory address, if we want what is stored at that address we need to use the indirection (de-reference) operator.

Below (from bottom of page 615):

232

Above: Place Figure 10-6 (page 616) – The graphic illustrates how different data types require a differing amounts of memory. Adding one to a pointer will advance to the next element in the array based on the type of the array.

Memory Allocation Functions

We have already discussed the limitations of static array declaration. With statically declared arrays the programmer must know the size of their data needs in advance, or make an approximation which leaves us with two potential problems:

Static (fixed) allocation of memory is done prior to the compiling of the program. A dynamic allocation of memory can be done while the program is running and utilizes **predefined functions** that can both allocate and free (de-allocate) memory.

- The `malloc` (memory allocation, found in `stdlib.h`) function will allocate a given number of bytes of memory. A pointer must be used to reference the starting address of the newly allocated memory.

233

Example – Ask the user for the number of experiments which represents the amount of integer data we need to store.

```
int amtData();
void getData(int*, int);
void printData(int*, int);

int main()
{
    int numExp;  //NUMBER OF EXPERIEMENTS
    int *data;   //INT PTR TO REFERENCE ALLOCATED MEMORY BASED ON numExp

    numExp = amtData();
    data = (int *)malloc(sizeof(int) * numExp);
    getData(data, numExp);
    printData(data, numExp);

    return(0);
}
```

How do you describe the expression being sent as a parameter to the `malloc` function?

```
void printData(int *d, int n)
{
    int lcv;

    for(lcv = 0; lcv < n; lcv++)
    {
        printf("Data value #%d: %d\n", lcv + 1, d[lcv]);
    }
}
```

```
void getData(int *d, int n)
{
    int lcv;

    for(lcv = 0; lcv < n; lcv++)
    {
        printf("Enter value #%d: ", lcv + 1);
        scanf("%d", &d[lcv]);
    }
}

int amtData()
{
    int n;

    printf("Please enter number of experiments: ");
    scanf("%d", &n);

    return(n);
}
```

Note: While the variable is defined as an integer pointer in the function header it is used as if it were an array for the remainder of the function.

Searching for a Sub-string

Many problems require locating within a string with a given sub-string. For example, given a string and sub-string determine the number of times the sub-string appears in the string.

```
Enter the string: ATATATA
Enter the substring: AT
The string AT appears 3 time(s) in the string ATATATA.

Enter the string: ATATATAT
Enter the substring: TA
The string TA appears 3 time(s) in the string ATATATAT.

Enter the string: ATATA
Enter the substring: ATA
The string ATA appears 2 time(s) in the string ATATA.
```

- The strstr function accepts two character arrays as parameters (the string and sub-string) and returns the location in the string of the sub-string.

For example, **Figure 11-20 on page 702**. The location returned is assigned to the character pointer s1.

If the sub-string is not present then then the pointer is assigned a value of NULL (essentially a defined value of zero).

- `pt = strstr(str, sub);`

If the character pointer pt is not NULL, then we have found one location of the sub-string (sub) in the string (str).

How do we find the next occurrence of sub in the string?

How do we know when we want to stop?

Solution:

```
#include<string.h>

#define SUBSTR 20
#define STRING 50

void getStr(char[], char[]);
int ctStrings(char[], char[]);
void cutString(char[]);
```

236

```c
int main()
{
    char sub[SUBSTR + 1]; //STRING FOR SUBSTRING
    char string[STRING + 1]; //STRING INPUT
    int subN = 0; //NUMBER OF SUBSTRINGS APPEARING IN DATA FILE

    getStr(string, sub);

    subN = ctStrings(string, sub);

    printf("The string %s appears %d time(s) in the string %s.\n", sub, subN, string);

    return(0);
}
int ctStrings(char str[], char sub[])
{
    int count = 0; //NUMBER OF MATCHES
    char *pt;      //LOCATION OF SUB IN STR

    pt = strstr(str, sub); //TRY TO FIND FIRST SUB STARTING AT STR INDEX ZERO

    while(pt != NULL)   //pt == NULL WHEN NO (MORE) SUBs FOUND
    {
        count++;
        pt = strstr(pt + 1, sub);   //pt = strstr(pt + strlen(sub), str); NO OVERLAPPING!
    }

    return(count);
}
void getStr(char x[], char y[])
{
    printf("Enter the string: ");
    fgets(x, STRING, stdin);
    cutString(x);

    printf("Enter the substring: ");
    fgets(y, SUBSTR, stdin);
    cutString(y);
}

void cutString(char z[])
{
    int i = 0;

    while(z[i] != '\n')
    {
        i++;
    }
    z[i] = '\0';
}
```

237

U N I X   H A N D O U T

LIST CURRENT DIRECTORY CONTENTS

```
ls          lists the files in the current directory.

lsl         list all files in the current directory in the long format (includes file
            size and last edited).
```

DIRECTORY NAVIGATION AND MANIPULATION

```
cd lab01        change directory to lab01 directory (relative path name).

cd ..           change directory to the parent of current directory.

cd              change directory to the user's home directory.

cd ~/CS159/hw   change directory to /CS159/hw (full path name).

mkdir labs      creates directory labs.

rmdir labs      removes directory labs (directory must be empty).
```

FILE UTILITIES

```
more hw01.c             displays the file hw01.c one screen at a time.

rm  hw01.c              removes hw01.c from the current directory.

cp  hw01.c hw01B.c      makes a copy of hw01.c and names it hw01B.c

mv  lab01.c lab02.c     renames the file lab01.c to lab02.c

mv  lab01.c lab01/      file lab01.c will now be found only in the directory /lab01.
```

COMPILERS/COMMAND LINE MATLAB

```
gcc  lab05.c        compiles the C program lab05.c.

octave  lab10.m     runs the lab10.m file using the MATLAB emulator Octave.
```

ASSIGNMENT SUBMISSION

```
submit      start the submission script to submit a file to an assignment.
```

USEFUL UNIX PROMPT COMMANDS

```
!v                      re-executes the last command beginning with a v.
!g                      re-executes the last command beginning with a g.
!!                      re-executes the most recent command.
Up-arrow, down-arrow    scroll through previously executed commands.
```

LOGGING OFF

```
logout      always use this command to terminate your connection to guru.
```

VI EDITOR

ENTER AND EXIT vi

```
vi f1.c          initiates an edit session on the file f1.c

:q!              will exit and discard the changes.
:w               will update the file being edited without exiting.
:wq              will write (save) and quit (exit) the text editor.
```

ENTER INSERT MODE

```
a                appends text after the cursor position.
i                inserts text before the cursor position.
o                opens a new line below the cursor position.
O                Opens a new line above the cursor position.
```

EXIT INSERT MODE

```
<ESC>            type escape to re-enter command mode.
```

CURSOR MOVEMENT (Arrows work in both insert and command mode)

```
G                moves the cursor to the last line in the file.
10G              moves the cursor to line 10.
:10              moves the cursor to line 10.
```

TEXT MOVING/EDITING COMMANDS

```
yy               Yank a copy of a line, place it in a buffer.
10yy             Yank 10 lines and places them in a buffer.

p                put the last item yanked after the cursor.
P                Put the last item yanked before the cursor.

dd               deletes the current line.
4dd              deletes the next four lines.

x                deletes the character under the cursor.
J                join the current line with the line below.
```

OTHER COMMANDS IN vi

```
u                undoes the last command that changed the buffer.

/string          Searches for "string" in the text file.
```

USEFUL EDITING TOOLS

```
:set paste       move to paste mode (shut off indenting). [F2 may work too]
:set nu          turn on line numbers.  Use :set nonu to turn off line numbers.
gg=G             format/indent entire file
```

ADDING COURSE HEADERS

```
hmlb             Insert MATLAB lab assignment header.
hlb              Insert C lab assignment header.
hhw              Insert C homework assignment header.
hfx              Insert C user-defined function header.
```

CS 159 – Spring 2018
Lecture Quiz Difficulty Report

Today's Date:

Your Name:

Your ITaP Career Account Username (DO NOT WRITE YOUR PASSWORD):

Quiz Answers:

By submitting this form I am acknowledging the following:
1. This is the only time I can use this form this semester.
2. I must submit this form at the end of the lecture quiz during which the difficulty was experienced.
3. I must show photo identification at the time I submit this form.
4. It is my responsibility to determine the source of the difficulty I experienced today and to get it resolved prior to the next lecture quiz. If the issue cannot be resolved in time for the next quiz I will visit the office hours of William Crum with a written detailed description of the situation.
5. Replacement iClickers can be registered on the course Blackboard site.

Your Signature:

CS 159 - Important Information

My Lab Instructor's Name:			
My Lab CRN for Submission:			
My Lecture Seat Assignment:	Team #1	Team #2	Team #3
My Midterm #1 Seat Assignment:			
My Midterm #2 Seat Assignment:			
Final Examination Seat Assignment:			
iClicker Serial Number:	• Remember to register your clicker on Blackboard! • Those with older clickers can contact ITaP (itap@purdue.edu) for assistance if your serial number is no longer readable.		

iClicker Channel/Frequency:	**How to set your channel/frequency:**
	1. Hold down the power button.
	   ○ Old clickers will blink (blue light), newer clickers will request that you SET FREQ.
	2. Release power button.
	3. Click the first character of the frequency.
	4. Click the second character of the frequency.
	   ○ Old clickers should produce a green light, newer clicker should show a check mark plus the name of the course on the screen.		